SONGS THE HEART REMEMBERS

The International Library of Music

Prepared under the Supervision of
THE EDITORIAL BOARD
of THE UNIVERSITY SOCIETY

ALBUM OF THE

World's Best Home Songs

WITH

INVITATION TO THE PIANO

by

ARNOLD BROIDO AND FELIX GREISSLE

with a Foreword by
IRWIN FREUNDLICH
Juillard School of Music

1963

THE UNIVERSITY SOCIETY, INC.
Educational Publishers since 1897
NEW YORK

THE UNIVERSITY SOCIETY INC
FOUNDED 1897

Manufactured in the U.S.A.

A Word About this Volume

WE TAKE pleasure in adding to our distinguished INTERNATIONAL LIBRARY OF MUSIC this volume of songs for singing in fellowship around a piano. They are songs the whole family will enjoy singing because many of them have also been favorites of our parents and grandparents, yet they are as popular and well-loved today as they ever were. Singing them together will contribute to the happy experiences of families as they gather around the piano. The young music student will enjoy accompanying them and perhaps singing along with them as heartily as the rest.

Acknowledgment

WE WANT to record here our grateful appreciation of the cooperative spirit of the EDWARD B. MARKS MUSIC CORPORATION in contributing to this volume. Their experience as publishers of popular music for over sixty years has been of invaluable help to us in assembling these songs. In addition to their good judgment in advising us, they have been most generous in granting us permission to reproduce many of their famous selections.

THE UNIVERSITY SOCIETY INC
FOUNDED 1897

Table of Contents

American Ballads and Folk Songs

Songs of Other Nations

Favorite Songs of Many Lands

Gilbert and Sullivan

Rounds

Lullabies

Negro Songs and Spirituals

Christmas Songs and Carols

Hymns and Other Songs of Devotion

American Patriotic Songs

Old Folks at Home

STEPHEN C. FOSTER
Arr. by P. Gallico

Moderato espressivo

p

1. Way down up - on the Swa - nee ri - ver, Far, far a - way, There's where my heart is
2. All 'round the lit - tle farm I wan - der'd, When I was young; Then man - y hap - py
3. One lit - tle hut a - mong the bush - es, One that I love, Still sad - ly to my

pp

turn - ing ev - er; There's where the old folks stay. All up and down the whole cre - a - tion,
days I squan - der'd, Man - y the songs I sung. When I was play - ing with my broth - er
mem - 'ry rush - es, No mat - ter where I rove. When shall I see the bees a - hum - ming,

Sad - ly I roam, Still long - ing for the old plan - ta - tion, And for the old folks at home.
Hap - py was I, Oh, take me to my kind old moth - er, There let me live and — die.
All 'round the comb? When shall I hear the ban - jo strum - ming, Down in my good old — home.

CHORUS

p con espress.

All the world is sad and drea - ry, Ev - 'ry - where I roam,

rit.

O! dar - kies how my heart grows wea - ry, Far from the old folks at home.

Little Annie Rooney

By MICHAEL NOLAN
Arr. by George Snowhill

Tempo di Valse
1. A win - ning way, a pleas- ant smile, Dressed so
2. The par - lor's small, but neat and clean, And set
3. We've been en - gaged close on a year, The hap -
neat but quite in style, Mer - ry chaff your time to wile, Has
with taste so seldom seen, And you can bet the household queen, Is
py time is drawing near, I'll wed the one I love so dear,
Lit - tle An - nie Roon - ey. Ev - 'ry ev' - ning rain or
Lit - tle An - nie Roon - ey. The fire burns cheer - ful - ly and
Lit - tle An - nie Roon - ey. My friends de - clare I'm in a
shine, I make a call twixt eight and nine, On her who
bright, As a fam' - ly cir - cle round each night, We form and
jest, Un - til the time comes will not rest, But one who

short - ly will be mine, Lit- tle An - nie Roon - ey.
ev - 'ry one's de - light, Is Lit- tle An - nie Roon - ey.
knows its val - ue best, Is Lit- tle An - nie Roon - ey.
CHORUS
She's my sweet - heart, I'm her beau;
She's my An - nie, I'm her Joe,
Soon we'll mar - ry, nev - er to part,
Lit - tle An - nie Roon-ey is my Sweet - heart!

Red River Valley

N. E. PEARSON
Arr. by G. M. Compagno

Slowly, with expression
mp
1. From this val - ley they say you are go - ing, I shall miss your sweet face and your
2. I have prom-ised you dar-ling that nev - er, Will the words from my lips cause you
mp
smile, Just be - cause you are wea - ry and tir - ed, You are
pain, And my life it will be yours for - ev - er, If you
chang - ing your range for a - while. I've been think - ing a long time my
on - ly would love me a - gain. There nev - er could be such a
dar - ling! Of the sweet words you nev - er would say, Now a -
long - ing, In the heart of a poor cow - boy's breast, As
las, must the fond hopes all van - ish? For they say you are go - ing a - way.
dwells in the heart you are break - ing, As I wait in my home in the West.

REFRAIN
Then come sit here a-while ere you leave us,— Do not hast-en to bid us a-dieu,— Just re-
mem-ber the Red Riv-er Val-ley,— And the cow-boy who loved you so true.—

Shoo Fly

Arr. by
Arthur Fields and Fred Hall

Not too slow

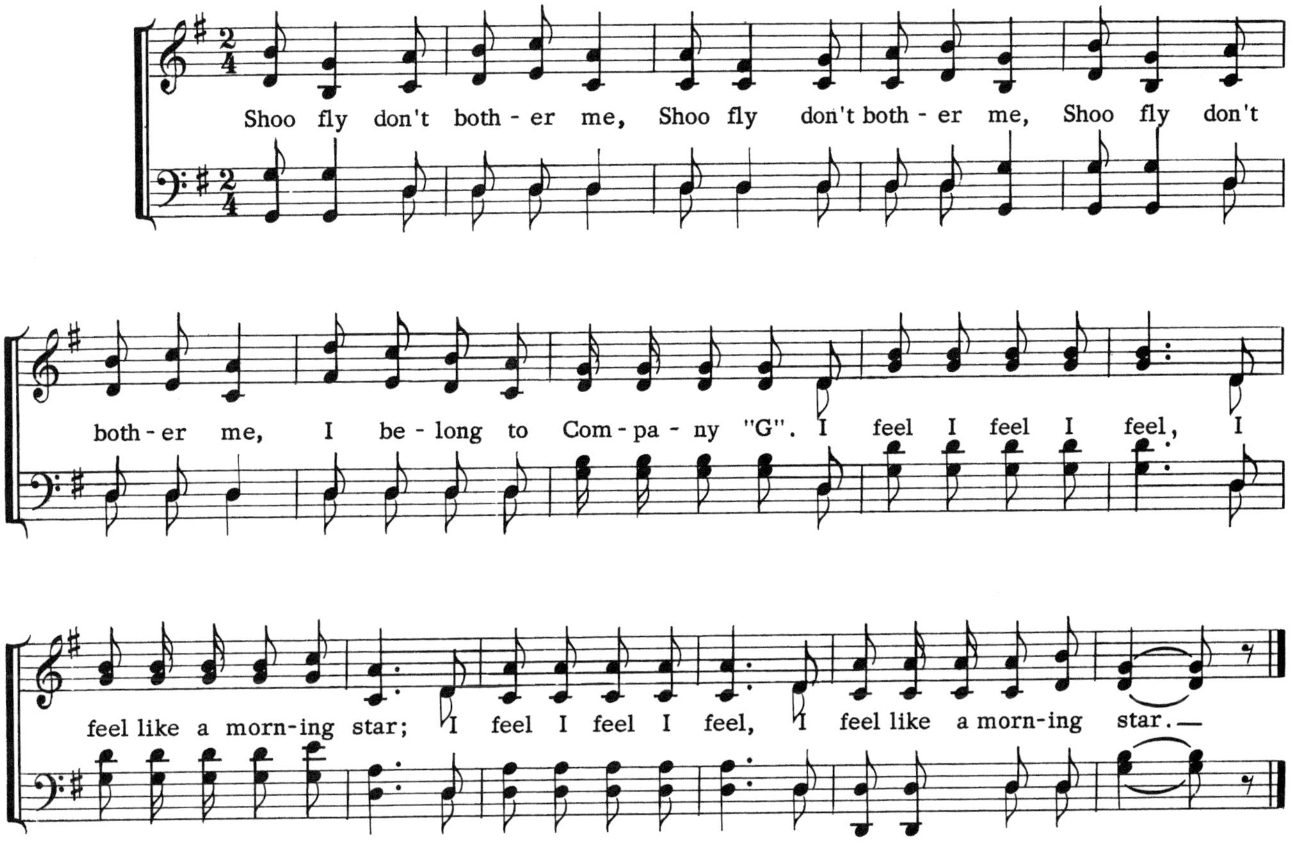

Shoo fly don't both-er me, Shoo fly don't both-er me, Shoo fly don't
both-er me, I be-long to Com-pa-ny "G". I feel I feel I feel, I
feel like a morn-ing star; I feel I feel I feel, I feel like a morn-ing star.—

On Top of Old Smoky

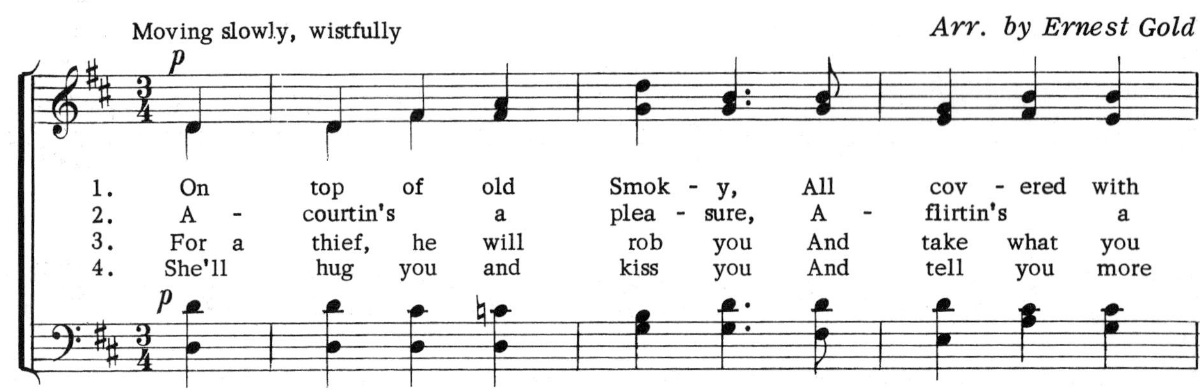
Moving slowly, wistfully
Arr. by Ernest Gold
p
1. On top of old Smok - y, All cov - ered with
2. A - courtin's a plea - sure, A - flirtin's a
3. For a thief, he will rob you And take what you
4. She'll hug you and kiss you And tell you more
p

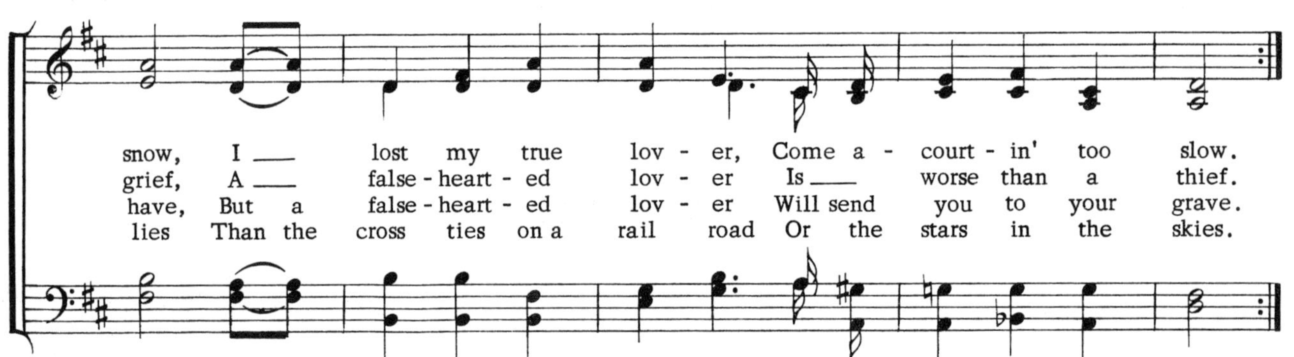
snow, I ___ lost my true lov - er, Come a - court - in' too slow.
grief, A ___ false - heart - ed lov - er Is ___ worse than a thief.
have, But a false - heart - ed lov - er Will send you to your grave.
lies Than the cross ties on a rail road Or the stars in the skies.

The Little Mohee

1. As I went out walking
Alone one fine day,
I got awful lonesome
As the day passed away,
I sat down a-musing
Alone on the grass,
When who should walk by me
But a sweet Indian lass.

2. She came and sat by me,
And took hold of my hand,
Said, "You sure are a stranger
In a far strange land."
She asked me to marry,
And offered her hand,
Said, "My pappy's a chieftain
All over this land."

3. I answered and told her
That it never could be
'Cause I had a sweetheart
In my own country—
"I will not forsake her
For I know she loves me;
Her heart is as true
As little Mohee."

4. At home with relations
I tried for to see,
But there wasn't a one
Like my little Mohee.
The girl I had trusted
Proved untrue to me
So I sailed back o'er the ocean
To my lovely Mohee.

Clementine

By PERCY MONTROSE
Arr. by Harry Henneman

Moderato
1. In a cav - ern in a can - yon, Ex - ca - vat - ing for a
2. Light she was, and like a fair - y, And her shoes were num-ber
3. Drove she duck - lings to the wa - ter Ev - 'ry morn - ing just at

mine, Dwelt a min - er for - ty nin - er, And his daugh - ter Cle - men-
nine, Her - ring box - es with - out top - ses, San - dals were for Cle - men-
nine, Hit her - foot a - gainst a splin - ter Fell in - to the foam - ing

tine;
tine; Oh my dar - ling, oh my dar - ling, oh my dar - ling Cle - men -
brine.

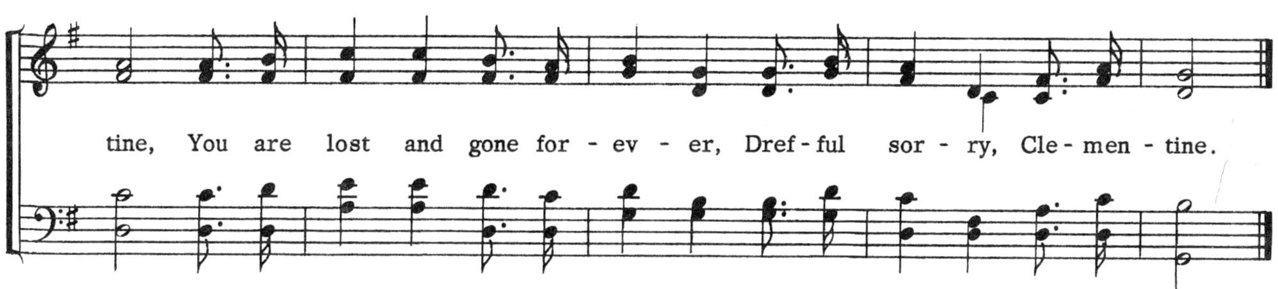
tine, You are lost and gone for - ev - er, Dref - ful sor - ry, Cle - men - tine.

Grandfather's Clock

HENRY C. WORK
Arr. by G. M. Compagno

Moderately.
1. My Grand - fa - ther's clock was too large for the shelf, So it
2. In watch - ing its pen - du - lum swing to and fro, Man - y
3. My Grand - fa - ther said that of those he could hire, Not a
4. It rang an a - larm in the dead of the night, An a -
stood nine - ty years on the floor; It was tall - er by half than the
hours had he spent while a boy; And in child - hood and man - hood the
ser - vant so faith - ful he found; For it wast - ed no time, and had
larm that for years had been dumb; And we knew that his spir - it was
old man him-self, Tho it weighed not a pen - ny weight more. It was
clock seemed to know, And to share both his grief and his joy. For it
but one de - sire: At the close of each week to be wound. And it
plum - ing its flight, That his hour of de - part - ure had come. Still the
bought on the morn of the day that he was born And was al - ways his treas -ure and
struck twen-ty four when he en - tered at the door, With a bloom-ing and beau - ti - ful
kept in its place, not a frown up - on its face, And its hands nev -er hung by its
clock kept the time, with a soft and muf-fled chime, As we sil - ent - ly stood by his
pride; But it stopp'd short nev-er to go a - gain, When the old man died.
bride, But it stopp'd short nev-er to go a - gain, When the old man died.
side; But it stopp'd short nev-er to go a - gain, When the old man died.
side; But it stopp'd short nev-er to go a - gain, When the old man died.

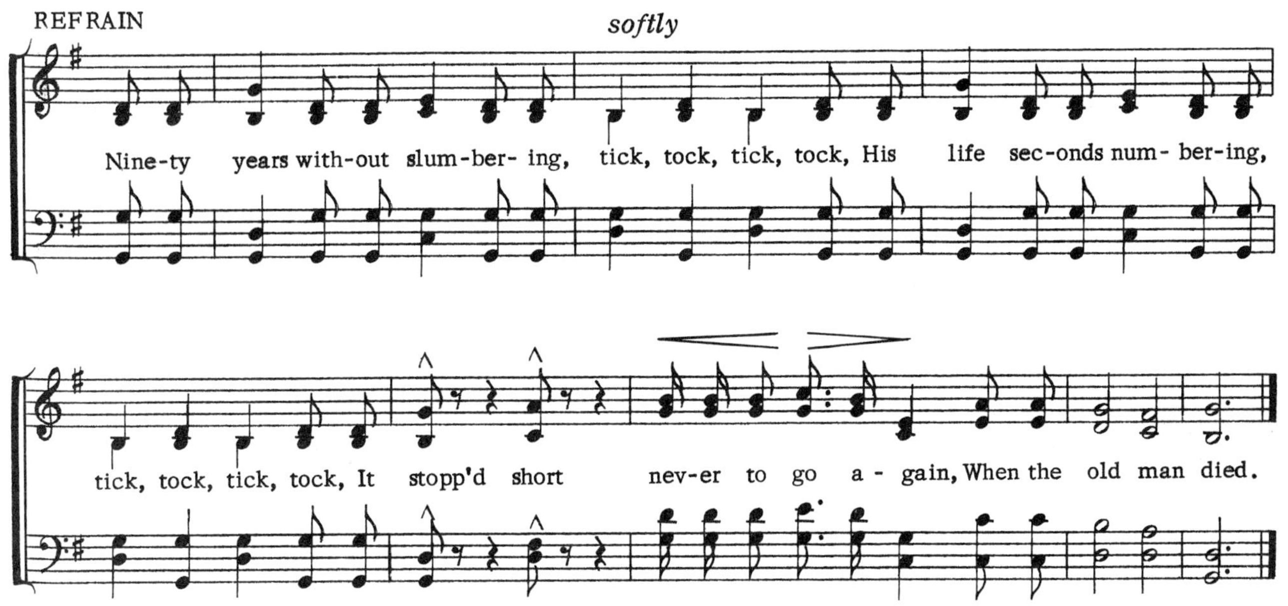
REFRAIN
softly
Nine-ty years with-out slum-ber-ing, tick, tock, tick, tock, His life sec-onds num-ber-ing,
tick, tock, tick, tock, It stopp'd short nev-er to go a - gain, When the old man died.

Hail, Hail, the Gang's All Here

SIR ARTHUR SULLIVAN
Arr. by Eleanore Dolores

With spirit.

Hail, hail — the gang's all here, What the heck do

we care, What the heck do we care, Hail, hail — the

gang's all here, What the heck do we care now? —

The Man on the Flying Trapeze

By ALFRED LEE and
GEORGE LEYBOURNE
Arr. by G. M. Groene
Waltz tempo
1. Once I was hap - py but now I'm for - lorn,
2. Now this man by name was Sig - nor Bon - i Slang,
3. Her fath - er and moth - er were both on my side,
like an old coat that is tat - ter'd and torn, Left in this
Tall, big and hand - some, as well made as Chang, Where-e'er he
And ve - ry hard tried to make her my bride, Her fath - er he
wide world to fret and to mourn, Be - trayed by a maid in her
ap - peared the hall loud - ly rang, With o - va - tion from all peo - ple
sighed and her moth- er she cried To see her throw her - self a -
teens. Now this girl that I lov'd she was hand
there. He'd smile from the bar on all peo - ple be -
way. 'Twas all no a - vail, she went there ev - 'ry
some, And I tried all I knew her to please. But I nev - er could
low, And one night he smiled on my love. She winked back at
night, And threw him bou - quets on the stage, Which caused her to

please her one quar - ter so well, As the man on the fly - ing tra - peze.
him and she shout-ed "brav - o," As he hung by his nose up a - bove.
meet him how he ran me down, To tell it would take a whole page.
Oh! He flies through the air with the great-est of ease, This dar - ing young
Last Chorus She floats through the air with the great-est of ease, You'd think her a
man on the fly - ing tra - peze, His move-ments are grace- ful, All
man on the fly - ing tra - peze, She does all the work While he
girls he does please And my love he has stol - en a - way.
sure takes his ease, And that's what's be - come of my love.

4. One night I,as usual, went to her dear home,
Found there her mother and father alone,
I asked for my love, and soon 'twas made known,
To my horror that she'd run away.
She packed up her boxes and eloped in the night.
With him with the greatest of ease,
From two stories high he had lowered her down
To the ground on his flying trapeze.

5. Some months after that I went into a hall,
To my surprise I found there on the wall.
A bill in red letters which did my heart gall,
That she was appearing with him.
He'd taught her gymnastics and dressed her in tights,
To help him to live at his ease,
He'd made her assume a masculine name,
And now she goes on the trapeze.

Listen to the Mocking Bird

ALICE HAWTHORNE
Arr. by G. M. Groene
Moderately
1. I'm dream-ing now of Hal-lie, sweet Hal-lie, sweet Hal-lie, I'm
2. Ah! well I yet re - mem-ber, re - mem-ber, re - mem-ber, Ah!
3. When the charms of spring a- wak-en, a - wak -en, a - wak -en, When
dream-ing now of Hal -lie for the thought of her is one that nev-er dies; She's
well I yet re - mem-ber, When we gath-ered in the cot- ton, side by side; 'Twas
the charms of spring a- wak- en And the mock-ing bird is sing-ing on the bough, I
sleep - ing in the val -ley, the val -ley, the val -ley, She's
in the mild Sep - tem-ber, Sep - tem - ber, Sep - tem-ber, 'Twas
feel like one for - sak - en, for - sak - en, for - sak -en, I
sleep - ing in the val- ley, And the mock-ing bird is sing-ing where she lies.
in the mild Sep - tem-ber, And the mock-ing bird is sing-ing far and wide.
feel like one for - sak- en, Since my Hal - lie is no long-er with me now.
CHORUS
Lis - ten to the mock - ing bird, Lis - ten to the mock - ing bird, The

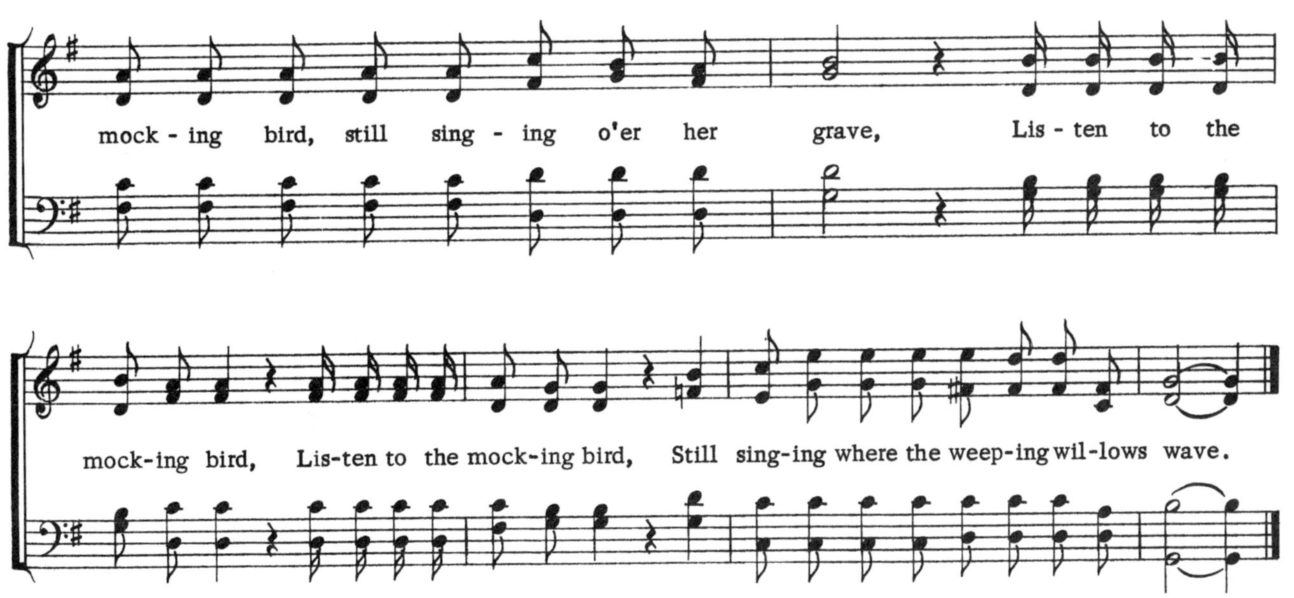
mock - ing bird, still sing - ing o'er her grave, Lis - ten to the
mock-ing bird, Lis-ten to the mock-ing bird, Still sing-ing where the weep-ing wil-lows wave.

There'll Be a Hot Time in the Old Town Tonight

JOE HAYDEN

THEO. A. METZ
Arr. by G. M. Compagno

Lively

When you hear dem a bells go ding, ling, ling, All join 'round And

sweet- ly you must sing, and when the verse am through, In the cho - rus all join

in, There'll be a hot time in the old town to - night my ba - by night

1. 2.

Ben Bolt

THOMAS DUNN ENGLISH
NELSON KNEASS
Semplice.
1. Oh! don't you re-mem-ber sweet Al-ice Ben Bolt, Sweet_ Al - ice whose hair was so brown,
2. And don't you re-mem-ber the school, Ben Bolt, With the mas -ter so kind and so true,
3. There is change in the things I loved, Ben Bolt, They have changed from the old to the new;
Who_ wept with de-light when you gave her a smile, And trem-bled with fear at your frown?
And the sha - ded_ nook by the run - ning brook, Where the fair- est wild flow-ers grew?
But I feel in the depths of my spir- it the truth, There nev-er was change in_ you.
In the old church-yard, in the val-ley, Ben Bolt, In a cor- ner ob -scure and a - lone,
Grass_ grows on the mas-ter's grave,_ Ben Bolt, The_ spring of the brook is_ dry,
Twelve_ months_ twen- ty have past,_ Ben Bolt, Since_ first we were friends yet I hail
They have fit - ted a slab of the gra-nite so gray, And sweet Al-ice lies un - der the stone,
And of all_ the boys who were school-mates then, There are on - ly you and_ I,
Thy_ pre-sence a bless-ing, thy friend-ship a truth, Ben_ Bolt of the salt sea_ gale,

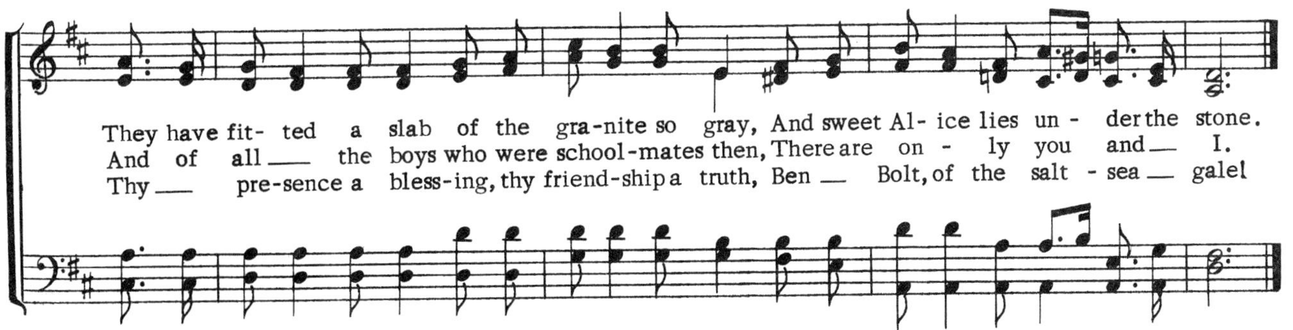
They have fit- ted a slab of the gra-nite so gray, And sweet Al- ice lies un - der the stone.
And of all ___ the boys who were school-mates then, There are on - ly you and ___ I.
Thy ___ pre-sence a bless-ing, thy friend-ship a truth, Ben ___ Bolt, of the salt - sea ___ gale!

Down in the Valley

Arranged by
ERNEST GOLD

With sentiment.

p

1. Down in the val - ley, the val - ley so
2. Writ - ing this let - ter, con - tain - ing three
3. If you don't love me, ___ love whom you
4. Ros - es love sun - shine, ___ vio - lets love

low, Hang your head o - ver, hear the wind blow. Hear the wind
lines, An - swer my ques - tion, will you be mine? Will you be
please, Throw your arms 'round me, give my heart ease. Give my heart
dew, An - gels in heav - en know I love you. Know I love

blow dear, ___ hear the wind blow, Hang your head o - ver, hear the wind blow.
mine, dear, ___ will you be mine? An -swer my ques - tion, will you be mine?
ease, dear, be- fore it's too late, Throw your arms 'round me, feel my heart break.
you, dear, ___ know I love you, An - gels in heav - en know I love you.

Polly Wolly Doodle

Lively
Solo or Unison
Arr. by G. M. Compagno
1. Oh, I went down South for to see my Sal,
2. Oh, my Sal she am a maid - en fair;
CHORUS
Sing Pol - ly wol - ly doo - dle all the day;
Solo
My Sal - ly am a spunk - y gal,
With laugh - ing eyes and curl - y hair,
CHORUS
Sing Pol - ly wol - ly doo - dle all the day.
Fare thee well, Fare - well, fare thee well, fare - well, fare thee
well my fair - y fay, For I'm goin' to Loui - si - a - na, For to
see my Su - sy - an - na, Sing Pol - ly wol - ly doo - dle all the day.

The Old Gray Mare

Arr. by
Arthur Fields and Fred Hall
Not too slow
The old gray mare she ain't what she used to be, ain't what she used to be, ain't what she used to be; the old gray mare she ain't what she used to be, man - y long years a - go.
CHORUS
Man-y long years a - go Man-y long years a - go The old gray mare she ain't what she used to be, ain't what she used to be, ain't what she used to be; the old gray mare she ain't what she used to be, man - y long years a - go.

Beautiful Dreamer

STEPHEN C. FOSTER
Arr. by G. M. Groene

Slowly with expression
1. Beau - ti - ful dream-er, wake un - to me Star-light and dew-drops are wait-ing for
2. Beau - ti - ful dream-er, out on the sea Mer-maids are chant-ing the wild lo - re -
thee, Sounds of the rude world heard in the day
lie, O - ver the stream - let va - pors are borne,
Lull'd by the moon-light have all passed a - way. Beau - ti - ful dream - er,
Wait - ing to fade at the bright, com - ing morn. Beau - ti - ful dream - er,
queen of my song, List while I woo thee with soft mel - o - dy;
beam on my heart, E'en as the morn on the stream-let and sea;
Gone are the cares of life's bu - sy throng, Beau-ti - ful dream-er, a-wake un - to
Then will all clouds of sor - row de - part, Beau-ti - ful dream-er, a-wake un - to
me, Beau - ti ful dream-er, a - wake un - to me.
me, Beau - ti ful dream-er, a - wake un - to me.

I Dream of Jeanie with the Light Brown Hair

STEPHEN FOSTER
Arr. by G. M. Groene

Moderately
1. I dream of Jea-nie with the light brown hair, Borne like a va - por
2. I long for Jea - nie with the day dawn smile, Ra - diant in glad - ness,
3. I sigh for Jea - nie but her light form strayed Far from the fond hearts
on the sum-mer air; I see her trip-ping where the bright streams play,
warm with win - ning guile; I hear her mel - o - dies, like joys gone by;
'round her na - tive glade; Her smiles have van-ished and her sweet songs flown,
Hap - py as the dai - sies that dance on her way. Man - y were the wild notes her
Sigh - ing 'round my heart o'er the fond hopes that die. Sigh - ing like the night wind and
Flit - ting like the dreams that have cheer'd us and gone. Now the nod-ding wild flow'rs may
mer-ry voice would pour, Man - y were the blithe birds that war - bled them o'er Oh! I
sob - bing like the rain, Wail-ing for the lost one that comes not a - gain Oh! I
with - er on the shore, While her gen-tle fing - ers will cull them no more Oh! I
rit.
dream of Jea - nie with the light brown hair, Float-ing like a va - por, on the soft sum-mer air.
long for Jea - nie and my heart bows low, Nev-er more to find her where the bright wa - ters flow.
sigh for Jea - nie with the light brown hair, Float-ing like a va - por, on the soft sum-mer air.
rit.

Sweet Marie

CY WARMAN

RAYMOND MOORE
Arr. by G. M. Compagno

Moderato
1. I've a se - cret in my heart, sweet Ma - rie; A tale I would im - part, love, to thee Ev - 'ry dai - sy in the dell, Knows my se-cret, knows it well, And yet I dare not tell, sweet Ma - rie.
2. In the morn when I a - wake, sweet Ma - rie; Seems to me my heart will break, love, to thee Ev - 'ry wave that shakes the shore Seems to sing it o'er and o'er, Seems to say that I a - dore, sweet Ma - rie.
When I hold your hand in mine, sweet Ma - rie A
When the sun - set tints the west, sweet Ma - rie And

feel - ing most di - vine comes to me,— All the world is full of spring, Full of
I sit down to rest, love, with thee, Ev - 'ry star that studs the sky, Seems to
war - blers on the wing, And I lis - ten while they sing, sweet Ma - rie.
stand and won - der why, They're so dim - mer than your eye, sweet Ma - rie.
Come to me, sweet Ma-rie, sweet Ma - rie, Come to me, Not be -
cause your face is fair, love, to see But your soul so pure and sweet, Makes my
hap - pi - ness com - plete, Makes me fal - ter at your feet, Sweet Ma - rie.
rall.

Aura Lee

GEORGE R. POULTON
Arr. by M. G. Groene

Moderately

1. As the black-bird in the spring, 'Neath the wil - low tree ___
2. On her cheek the rose was born; There was mu - sic when she spake; ___

Sat and pip'd, I heard him sing, Sing - ing Au - ra Lee.
In her eyes the rays of morn, With sud - den splen- dor break.

CHORUS

Au - ra Lee! Au - ra Lee! Maid of gold - en hair!

Sun - shine came a - long with thee, And swal - lows in the air.

The Monkey's Wedding

Arr. by
Arthur Fields and Fred Hall

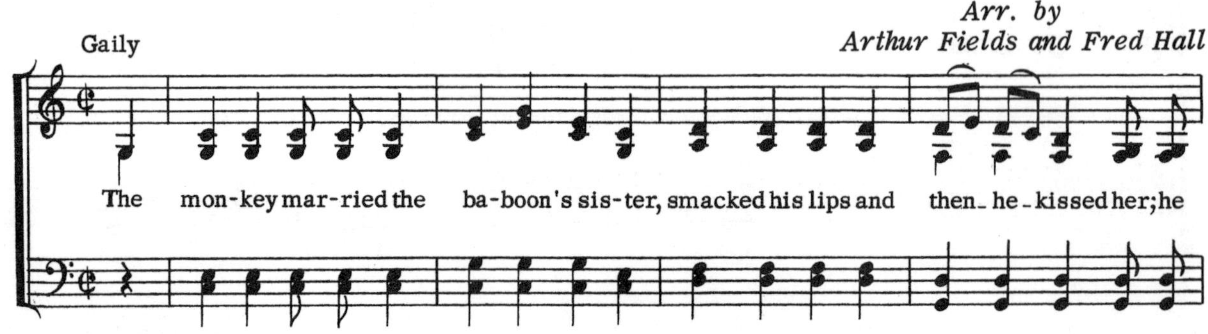
Gaily
The mon-key mar-ried the ba-boon's sis-ter, smacked his lips and then _ he _ kissed her; he

kissed so hard he raised a blis-ter, she set up a yell The brides-maid stuck on some court plas-ter it
stuck so fast it_ could-n't stick fast-er; sure-ly_'twas a_ sad dis-as-ter but_it_ soon got_ well.

In the Evening, by the Moonlight

JAS. A. BLAND
Arr. by. G. M. Compagno

Fairly slow

In the eve - ning by the moon - light, you could

hear the folks all sing-ing, In the eve - ning by the moon-light, you could

hear those ban - jos ring- ing, How the old folks would en - joy it, They would

sit all night and lis- ten, As we sang in the eve -ning by the moon- light.

A Spanish Cavalier

By W. D. HENDRICKSON

Arr. by George Snowhill

Moderato
1. A Span- ish Cav - a - lier stood in his re - treat, And on his gui-tar played a tune, dear; The mu - sic so sweet would oft - times re - peat the bless-ing of my coun - try and you dear.
2. I'm off to the war, to the war I must go, To fight for my coun - try and you dear; But if I should fall, in vain I would call, the bless-ing of my coun - try and you dear.
3. And when the war is o'er, to you I'll re - turn, a - gain to my coun - try and you dear; But if I be slain, you may seek me in vain, Up - on the bat - tle field you will find me.
CHORUS
Oh, say, Dar - ling, say, when I'm far a - way, Some-times you may think of me dear;
Bright sun-ny days will soon fade a - way, Re - mem-ber what I say and be true, dear.

The Vacant Chair

GEORGE F. ROOT

p Andante con espress.
1. We shall meet, but we shall miss him, There will be one va-cant chair; We shall
2. At our fire-side, sad and lone-ly, Oft - en will the bos- om swell At re -
3. True, they tell us wreaths of glo- ry Ev - er - more will deck his brow, But this
lin - ger to ca - ress him, While we breathe our eve - ning pray'r. When a
mem-brance of the sto - ry, How our no - ble Wil - lie fell; How he
soothes the an - guish on - ly Sweep - ing o'er our heart - strings now, Sleep to -
year a - go we gath-ered, Joy was in his mild blue eye, But a
strove to bear our ban - ner Thro' the thick - est of the fight, And up-
day, oh, ear - ly fall - en, In thy green and nar - row bed, Dir - ges
gold - en cord is sev - ered, And our hopes in ru - in lie.
hold our coun - try's hon - or, In the strength of man-hood's might.
from the pine and cy - press Min - gle with the tears we shed.
CHORUS
p dolce.
We shall meet, but we shall miss him, There will be one va - cant chair; We shall
lin - ger to ca - ress him, When we breathe our eve - ning pray'r.

Pop Goes the Weasel

Lively

Arr. by Ernest Gold

mf

1. All a-round the cob - bler's bench the monk - ey chased the wea - sel, The monk - ey thought 'twas all in fun, Pop goes the wea - sel! 2. A pen - ny for a spool of thread, A pen - ny for a nee - dle, That's the way the monk - ey goes, Pop goes the wea - sel!

(ad lib.)

There's a Little Wheel a-Turnin' in My Heart

Lightly and gaily
Arr. by Florence White
1. There's a lit - tle wheel a - turn - in' in my heart, There's a
2. There's a lit - tle song a - sing - in' in my heart, There's a

lit - tle wheel a - turn - in' in my heart, in my heart, in my
lit - tle song a - sing - in' in my heart, in my heart, in my
heart. There's a lit - tle wheel a - turn - in' in my heart.
heart. There's a lit - tle song a - sing - in' in my heart.

Where Did You Get That Hat?

JOS. J. SULLIVAN
Arr. by G. M. Compagno

Spiritedly

f

Where did you get that hat? Where did you get that tile? Is - 'nt it a nob-by one, And just the pro-per style, I should like to have one Just the same as that! Where-e'er I go they shout Hel - lo! Where did you get that hat?

Son of a Gambolier

QUARTET
Tenors
Basses
Come, join my hum-ble dit - ty, From Tip-pe-ry town I steer,_Like ev-'ry hon-est fel-low I
take my la - ger beer,_ Like ev - 'ry hon- est fel- low I take my whis-key clear; I'm a
ramb - ling rake of pov - er - ty, The son of a Gam - bo - lier. The
son of a, son of a, son of a, son of a, son of a Gam - bo - lier, The
son of a, son of a, son of a, son of a, son of a Gam - bo - lier; Like
ev - 'ry hon - est fel - low I take my whis - key clear, I'm a
3

ramb - ling rake of pov - er - ty, The son of a Gam - bo - lier.
In the Gloaming
Moderato
By ANNIE F. HARRISON
1. In the gloam - ing oh my dar - ling when the lights are dim and low
2. In the gloam - ing oh! my dar - ling think not bit - ter - ly of me
And the qui - et sha - dows fall - ing, soft - ly come and soft - ly go.
Though I passed a - way in si - lence, left you lone - ly set you free.
When the winds are sob - bing faint - ly with a gen - tle un-known woe,
For my heart was crushed with long - ing what had been could nev-er be.
Will you think of me and love me as you did once long a - go
It was best to leave you thus, dear, Best for you and best for me.

Daisy Bell

(A BICYCLE BUILT FOR TWO)

Words & Music by
HARRY DACRE

Arr. by George Snowhill

Waltz tempo
There is a flow - er with - in my heart,
We will go "tan - dem" as man and wife,
I will stand by you in "wheel" or woe,
Dai - sy! Dai - sy! Plant - ed one
Dai - sy! Dai - sy! "Ped - 'ling a -
Dai - sy! Dai - sy! You'll be the
day by a glanc - ing dart, Plant - ed by
way down the road of life, I and my
bell which I'll ring you know! Sweet lit - tle
Dai - sy Bell! Wheth - er she
Dai - sy Bell! When the road's
Dai - sy Bell! You'll take the
loves me or loves me not, Some - time it's
dark we can both de - spise, P'lice - men and
"lead" in each "trip" we take, Then if I

hard to tell: Yet I am
"lamps" as well; There are "bright
don't do well; I will per-
long - ing to share the lot, Of beau - ti - ful
lights" in the dazz - ling eyes, Of beau - ti - ful
mit you to use the brake, My beau - ti - ful
Dai - sy Bell.
Dai - sy Bell.
Dai - sy Bell.
Dai - sy,
Dai - sy, Give me your an - swer
do!
I'm half cra -

- zy, All for the love of you!
It won't be a styl - ish mar - riage,
I can't af - ford a car - riage,
But you'll look sweet, On the
seat, Of a bi - cy - cle built for two.
3

The Blue Tail Fly

CHORUS
Arr. by Florence White
Gaily.
Jim crack corn, I don't care,— Jim crack corn, I don't care,—
Jim crack corn, I don't care,— My mas- ter's gone a - way.——
Fine
With mock drama.
1. When I was young I used to wait on mas -ter and hand him his plate, And
2. When he rode out in the af - ter noon, I'd fol - low with a hick-'ry broom, The
3. One day he rode a - round the farm, The flies so num-'rous they did swarm, One
pass the bot-tle when he got dry, And brush a - way the blue tail fly.
po - ny be - ing ve - ry shy, When bit - ten by the blue tail fly.
chanced to bite him on the thigh, The de - vil take the blue tail fly.
D. C.

4. The pony run, he jump, he pitch,
He threw old master in the ditch,
He died and the jury wondered why,
The verdict was the blue tail fly.

5. Old master's gone now, let him rest,
They say all things are for the best;
But I'll never forget 'til the day I die
Old master and that blue tail fly.

I Ride an Old Paint

Loping along

Arr. by Florence White

1. I ride an old Paint, I lead an old Dan, I'm goin' to Mon - tan', for to throw the hoo - li - an, They feed in the cou - lees, they wa - ter in the draw, Their tails are all mat - ted, their backs are all raw.
2. Oh, when I die, take my sad - dle from the wall, Put it on my po - ny, lead him out of his stall. Tie my bones to his back, turn our faces to the west, And we'll ride the prai - rie that we love the best.
Ride a - round, lit - tle do - gies, ride a - round them slow, For the fie - ry and snuf - fy are a - rar - in' to go.

Good-by, Old Paint

Slow Waltz time
Arr. by M. G. Groene
mf My feet are in the stir - rups, My bri - dle's in my hand; Good -
bye, my lit - tle la - dy, My po - ny won't stand.
CHORUS (2nd time pp)
f
Good - bye Old Paint I'm a leav - in' Chey - enne,
cresc.
I'm a - leav - in' Chey - enne, I'm off for Mon - tan',
Melody
(2nd time pp)
Good bye, Old Paint, I'm a - leav - in' Chey - enne.

You Tell Me Your Dream

Lyric by
ALBERT H. BROWN
and SEYMOUR RICE

Music by
CHARLES N. DANIELS

Arr. by George Snowhill

CHORUS
You had a dream, well, I had one
too. I know mine's best 'cause it
was of you. Come, sweet-heart, tell
me, now is the time. You tell me
your dream, I'll tell you mine.

After the Ball

CHARLES K. HARRIS
Arr. by George Snowhill

Waltz tempo
Af - ter the ball is o - ver, Af - ter the
break of morn,
Af - ter the dan - cers leav -
ing, Af - ter the stars are gone;
Man - y a heart is ach - ing, if you could
read them all;
Man - y the hopes that have
van - ished Af - ter the ball.

The Erie Canal

Arr. by Felix Guenther

Not fast
f
mf
1. I've got a mule, her name is Sal. Fif-teen miles on the E - rie Ca - nal. She's a good old work - er and a good old pal, Fif - teen miles on the E - rie Ca - nal. We've hauled some barg - es in our day.
2. We bet-ter get a - long on our way, old gal; Fif-teen miles on the E - rie Ca - nal. 'Cause you bet your life I'd nev - er part with Sal, Fif - teen miles on the E - rie Ca - nal. Git up there mule here comes a lock.
mf
f

Filled with lum - ber, coal and hay, And we know ev' - ry
We'll make Rome 'bout six o' - clock, One more trip and
rit.
inch of the way, From Al - ba - ny to Buf - fa - lo.
back we'll go Right back home to Buf - fa - lo.
a tempo
f
Low bridge, ev' - ry - bo - dy down, Low bridge, for we're
go - ing through a town, And you'll al - ways know your neigh - bor, You'll
al - ways know your pal. If you've ev - er nav - i - gat - ed on the E - rie Ca - nal.

She'll Be Comin' Round the Mountain

Moderato

Arr. by George Snowhill

1. She'll be com - in' 'round the moun - tain when she comes,— She'll be com - in' 'round the moun - tain when she comes,— She'll be com - in' 'round the moun - tain, She'll be com - in' 'round the moun - tain, She'll be com - in' 'round the moun - tain when she comes.—
2. She'll be driv - in' six white hors - es when she comes,— She'll be driv - in' six white hors - es when she comes,— She'll be driv - in' six white hors - es, She'll be driv - in' six white hors - es, She'll be driv - in' six white hors - es when she comes.—

Say "Au Revoir," But Not "Good-by"

By HARRY KENNEDY
Arr. by Harry Henneman

Moderato
1. Say "Au Re - voir"— But not "Good - bye",— For part - ing brings— a bit - ter
2. The wa - ters glide,— the oars lie still,— A rip - pling laugh— a word at

sigh; — The past is gone, — though mem-'ry gives, — One cling-ing thought — the fu-ture
will; — 'Where an-gels fear, — fools dare to tread', — Shall live for years, — tho' past is
lives; — Our du-ty first, — love must not lead, — What might have been, — had fate de-
dead; — This one good-bye — must be our last, — The word is spoke, — the die is
creed; 'Twere bet-ter far — had we not met, — I loved you then, I love you yet.
cast; — But still my heart throbs wild with pain, And tho' we ne'er shall meet a-gain.
REFRAIN
Say "Au Re-voir", — But not "Good-bye" — Though past is dead, — love can-not die, — 'Twere bet-ter
far — had we not met, I loved you then, I love you yet.

Sweet Genevieve

GEORGE COOPER

HENRY TUCKER
Arr. by G. M. Groene

Moderately slow.
1. Oh! Gen-e-vieve I'd give the world To live a-gain the love-ly past! The rose of youth was dew im-pearled, But now it with-ers in the blast, I see thy face in ev-'ry dream, My wak-ing thoughts are full of thee; Thy glance is in the star-ry beam That falls a-long the sum-mer sea.
mp 2. Fair Gen-e-vieve my ear-ly love, The years but make thee dear-er far! My heart shall nev-er, nev-er rove: Thou art my on-ly guid-ing star, For me the past has no re-gret, What e'er the years may bring to me: I bless the hour when first we met, The hour that gave me love and thee.
Oh!
REFRAIN With expression.
Gen-e-vieve, sweet Gen-e-vieve, The days may come, the days may go, But still the hands of mem-'ry weave The bliss-ful dreams of long a-go.

When You and I Were Young, Maggie

By J. A. BUTTERFIELD

Arr. by Arthur Fields and Fred Hall

Moderato
1. I wan - der'd to - day to the hill Mag - gie, To watch the scene be - low The creek and the creak - ing old mill, Mag-gie, As we used to long long a - go. The
2. green grove is gone from the hill Mag - gie, When first the dais - ies sprung The creak - ing old mill is so still, Mag-gie, Since you and I were young And
1.
2.
now we are ag - ed and gray, Mag - gie, The trials of life are near - ly done Let's sing of the days that are gone, Mag - gie, When you and I were young.

Ta-ra-ra Boom-Dee-Ay

By HENRY J. SAYERS

Arr. by George Snowhill

With Humor
1. A — sweet Tux - e - do girl you see, Queen of swell so - ci - e - ty,
2. I'm a blush - ing bud of in - no-cence, Pa - pa says at big ex-pense,
Fond of fun as fond can be, When it's on the strict Q. T. I'm
Old maids say I have no sense, Boys de - clare I'm just im-mense, Be -
not too young, I'm not too old, Not too tim - id, not too bold,
-fore my song I do con- clude, I want it strict - ly un - der- stood, Tho'
Just the kind you'd like to hold, Just the kind for sport I'm told.
fond of fun, I'm nev - er rude, Tho' not too bad I'm not too good.
Ta - ra - ra Boom - dee-ay Ta - ra - ra Boom - dee-ay

Ta - ra - ra Boom - dee-ay Ta - ra - ra Boom - dee- ay

Ta - ra - ra Boom - dee- ay Ta - ra - ra Boom - dee-ay

1. 2.

Ta - ra- ra Boom-dee-ay Ta - ra - ra Boom-dee-ay I'm a Boom-dee-ay.

You're Not the Only Pebble on the Beach

Lyric by HARRY BRAISTED

Music by STANLEY CARTER

Arr. by George Snowhill

Marcia
"You're not the on - ly peb - ble on the beach! For there are oth -ers," said the

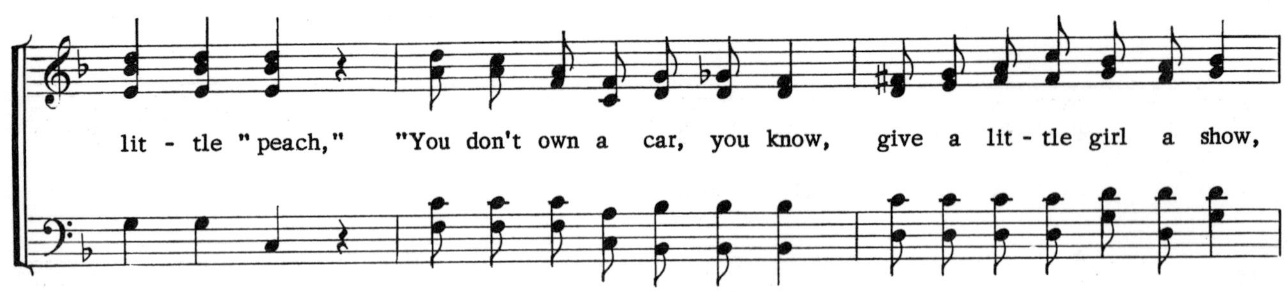
lit - tle "peach," "You don't own a car, you know, give a lit - tle girl a show,

You are not the on - ly peb - ble, there are lots of oth - er peb - bles,

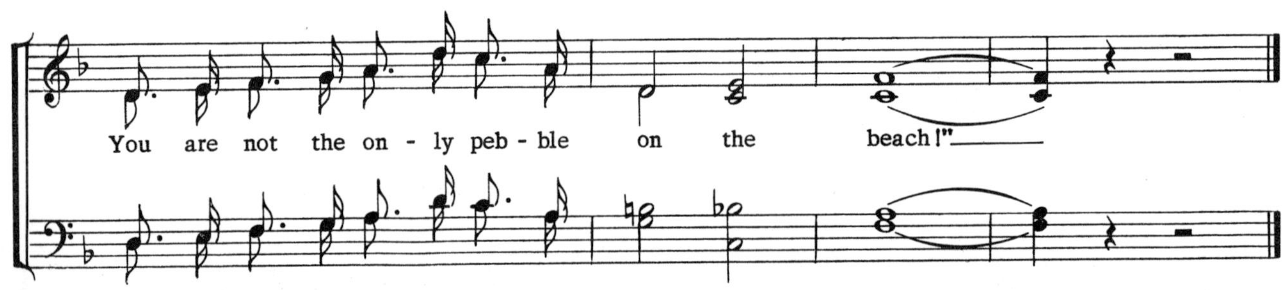
You are not the on - ly peb - ble on the beach!"

Nut Brown Maiden

Moderato
1. Nut brown maid - en, Thou hast a bright blue eye for love,
2. Nut brown maid - en, Thou hast a ru - by lip to kiss,

Nut brown maid - en, Thou hast a bright blue eye; A bright blue eye is thine, love! The
Nut brown maid - en, Thou hast a ru - by lip; A ru - by lip is thine, love! The

glance in it is mine, love! Nut brown maid - en, Thou hast a bright blue eye for love,
kiss - ing of it's mine, love! Nut brown maid - en, Thou hast a ru - by lip to kiss,

Nut brown maid - en, Thou hast a bright blue eye.
Nut brown maid - en, Thou hast a ru - by lip.

Kentucky Babe

Lyric by RICHARD HENRY BUCK

Music by ADAM GEIBEL

Arr. by George Snowhill

Tempo di Schottische
'Skeet-ers am a hum-min' on de hon-ey suck-le vine, Sleep, Ken-tuck-y
Babe! Sand-man am a com- in' to dis lit - tle babe of mine,

Sleep, Ken-tuck-y Babe! Sil-v'ry moon am shin-in' in de heab-ens up a-bove,
Bob-o-link am pin-in' fo' his lit-tle la-dy love, You is migh-ty luck-y,
Babe of old Ken-tuck-y, Close yo' eyes in sleep.
Fly a-way, fly a-way Ken-tuck-y Babe, fly a-way to rest,
Fly a-way, Lay yo' kin-ky, wool-ly head on yo' mam-my's breast.
Um Um close yo' eyes in sleep.

Silver Threads Among the Gold

Lyric by EBEN E. REXFORD

Music by H. P. DANKS

Dar - ling I am grow - ing old
Sil - ver threads a - mong the gold
Shine up - on my brow to day
Life is fad - ing fast a - way
But my dar - ling you will be will be
Al - ways young and fair to me
Yes my dar-ling you will be
Al - ways young and fair to me.

The Band Played On

JOHN F. PALMER

CHARLES B. WARD
Arr. by Paul Hill

Waltz tempo
Ca-sey would waltz with a straw- ber - ry blonde, And the band played on,
He'd glide 'cross the floor with the girl he a - dored, And the band
played on, But his brain was so load-ed it near-ly ex - plod -ed, The
poor girl would shake with a - larm. He'd ne'er leave the girl with the
straw - ber -ry curl, And the band played on.

Ida, Sweet as Apple Cider

Lyric by
EDDIE LEONARD
Music by
EDDIE MUNSON
Arr. by Oscar Catsiff
Moderato
mp
I - da sweet as ap - ple ci - der
I - da dear, you are
Sweet - er than all I know
I - da come out in the sil - v'ry
moon - light of love we'll whis - per so soft and low, we'll whis - per
soft and low, dear seems tho' can't live with - out you.
How I need you, so
Lis - ten Oh! hon - ey do! Ooo
I - da, I i - do
lize yer I - da, I love you, I - da, deed I do.

Love's Old Sweet Song

G. CLIFTON BINGHAM

J. L. MALLOY
Arr. by M. G. Groene

Quietly.
p
1. Once in the dear dead days be - yond re - call, When on the world the
2. E - ven to - day we hear love's song of yore, Deep in our hearts it
mists be - gan to fall, Out of the dreams that rose in hap - py throng,
dwells for - ev - er more; Foot - steps may fal - ter, wea - ry grow the way,
Low to our hearts love sang an old sweet song, And in the dusk where
Still we can hear it at the close of day. So to the end, when
fell the fire-light gleam, Soft - ly it wove it - self in - to our dream.
life's dim shad-ows fall, Love will be found the sweet-est song of all.
CHORUS
mp
Just a song at twi - light, When the lights are low; And the flick- 'ring

sha - dows Soft - ly come and go — Tho' the heart be wea - ry, Sad the day and
long, Still to us at twi - light Comes love's old song, Comes love's old sweet song.

Good Night, Ladies

Not too slow

1. Good - night La - dies! Good - night La - dies! Good - night La - dies! We're going to leave you now
2. Fare - well La - dies! Fare - well La - dies! Fare - well La - dies! We're going to leave you now
3. Sweet dreams La - dies! Sweet dreams La - dies! Sweet dreams La - dies! We're going to leave you now

Mer - ri - ly we roll a - long, Roll a - long, roll a - long, Mer - ri - ly we roll a - long, O - ver the dark blue sea.

Oh, Susanna!

Lively

STEPHEN C. FOSTER

1. I — come from Al - a - bam - my with my ban - jo on my knee I'm gwine to Lou - si - an - ny my — true love for to see. It —
2. rained all day the night I left the weath - er it was dry The sun so hot I froze to death Su - san - na don't you cry. —

CHORUS

Oh Su - san - na oh don't you cry for me I've come from Al - a - bam - my with my ban - jo on my knee. —

I Don't Want to Play in Your Yard

PHILIP WINGATE

H. W. PETRIE
Arr. by Sylvester Krouse

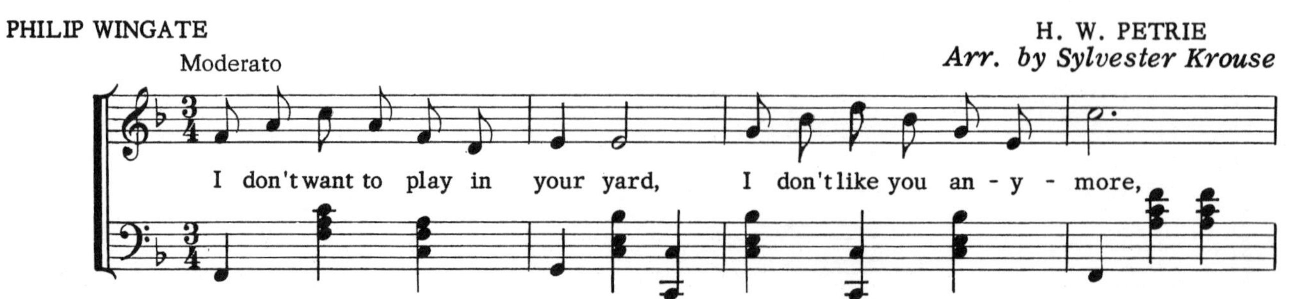
Moderato
I don't want to play in your yard, I don't like you an - y - more,

You'll be sor-ry when you see me Slid-ing down our cel-lar door,

You can't hol-ler down our rain barrel; You can't climb our ap-ple tree,

I don't want to play in your yard If you won't be good to me.

Go Tell Aunt Rhodie

Arr. by Florence White

Tenderly
1. Go tell Aunt Rho - die, Go tell Aunt Rho - die,
2. The one she's been sav - ing, The one she's been sav - ing, The
Go tell Aunt Rho - die, Her old gray goose is dead.
one she's been sav - ing, To stuff a feath - er bed.

My Old Kentucky Home

Words and Music by STEPHEN C. FOSTER
Arranged by P. Gallico.

Poco adagio.
The sun shines bright in the old Ken-tuck-y home, 'Tis sum-mer, the young folks are
gay. The corn - top's ripe and the mead- ow's in the bloom, While the
birds make mus- ic all the day; The young folks roll on the
lit - tle cab- in floor, All mer - ry, all hap- py and bright, By'n
by Hard Times comes a knock-ing at the door, Then my old Ken-tuck-y home, Good- night!

CHORUS
p
Weep no more, my la - dy, Oh! weep no more to - day! We will
p
sing one song for the old Ken-tuck-y home, For the old Ken-tuck-y home far a - way.
ritard.
D. C.
Shenandoah
Slowly, sustained.
Solo
All
1. Oh, Shen- an - doah, I long to hear you. A - way, my roll - ing
2. Oh, Shen-an - doah, I love your daugh-ter. A - way, my roll - ing
Solo
All
riv - er! Oh, Shen - an - doah, I can't get near you. A - way, a -
riv - er! She lives a - cross the storm- y wa - ter. A - way, a -
way, I'm bound a - way, 'Cross the wide Mis- sou - ri!
way, I'm bound a - way, 'Cross the wide Mis- sou - ri!

The Mermaid

Moderato
Arr. by Andor Pinter
mf
1. 'Twas Fri - day morn when we set sail, And we were not far from the land,
2. Then out spake the cap-tain of our gal-lant ship, And a well spo-ken man was he:
3. Then out spake the cook of our gal-lant ship, And a fat old cook-ie was he:
4. Then out spake the boy of our gal-lant ship, And a well spo-ken lad-die was he:
5. "Oh! the moon shines bright and the stars give light; Oh! my mam-my'll be look-ing for me;
6. Then three times a - round went our gal-lant ship, And three times a - round went she;
When the cap - tain spied a love-ly mer - maid, With a comb and a glass in her hand.
"I have mar - ried me a wife in Sa-lem town, And to - night she a wid - der will be."
"I care much more for my kett -les and my pots, Than I do for the depths of the sea."
"I've a fa - ther and a moth-er in Bos-ton cit -y, But to - night they child - less will be."
She may look, she may weep, she may look to the deep, She may look to the bot-tom of the sea."
Then three times a - round went our gal - lant ship, And she sank to the depths of the sea.
CHORUS
Tenors
f
Oh! the o - cean waves may roll, And the storm - y winds may blow, While
we poor sail - ors go skip-ping to the tops, And the land lub-bers lie down be -

low, be-low, be-low, And the land lub - bers lie down be - low.
D. C.

Gaudeamus Igitur

Andante

1. Gau - de - a - mus i - gi - tur, Ju - ve - nes dum su - mus;
2. U - bi sunt, qui an - te nos In mun-do fue - re?
3. Vi - vat a - ca - de - mi - a, Vi - vant pro - fes - so - res,

post ju - cun - dam ju - ven - tu - tem, Post mo - les - tam se - nec-tu - tem
Tran- se - as ad su - pe - ros, A - be - as ad in - fe - ros,
Vi - vat mem - brum quod-li - bet, Vi - vant mem - bra quæ - li - bet,

nos ha - be - bit hu - mus, nos ha - be - bit hu - mus.
Qu - os si vis vi - dere, Qu - os si vis vi - dere.
Sem - per sint in flo - re, Sem-per sint in flo - re.

De Camptown Races

STEPHEN FOSTER
Arr. by G. M. Compagno

Fast
1.De Camp-town la - dies sing dis song Doo - dah! Doo - dah!
2.De long - tail fil - ly and de big black hoss, Doo - dah! Doo - dah!
3.Old mu - ley cow come on to de track, Doo - dah! Doo - dah!
De Camp-town race track five miles long, Oh! doo - dah day!
Dey fly de track, an dey both cut a - cross, Oh! doo - dah day!
De bob - tail fling her ob - er his back, Oh! doo - dah day!
I come down dah wid my hat caved in, Doo - dah! Doo - dah!
De blind hoss stick - en in a big mud hole, Doo - dah! Doo - dah!
Den fly a - long like a rail - road car, Doo - dah! Doo - dah!
I go back home wid a pock-et full of tin, Oh! doo - dah day!
Can't touch bot-tom wid a ten - foot pole, Oh! doo - dah day!
Run - nin' a race wid a shoot-in' star, Oh! doo - dah day!
CHORUS
Gwine to run all night! Gwine to run all day! I'll

bet my mon-ey on de bob - tail nag, Some- bo - dy bet on de bay.

I've Been Working on the Railroad

Traditional
Arr. by M. G. Groene

Marcia

I've been work-ing on the rail - road All the live long day,—

I've been work- ing on the rail - road To pass the time a - way.—

Don't you hear the whis- tle blow - ing, Rise up so ear - ly in the morn?—

Don't you hear the cap - tain shout - ing; "Di - nah, come blow your horn?"—

Home on the Range

Arr. by H. S. Krouse

Moderato
1. Oh give me a home where the buf - fa - lo roam, Where the
2. Where the air is so pure, the zeph - yrs so free, And the
3. How oft - en at night when the heav - ens are bright, With the
4. Then I would not ex - change my home on the range, Where the
deer and the an - te - lope play, Where sel - dom is heard a dis -
breez - es so balm - y and light; I would not ex - change my
light of the glit - ter -ing stars, Have I stood there a - mazed and
deer and the an - te - lope play, Where sel - dom is heard a dis -
cour - ag - ing word, And the skies are not cloud - y all day, (all the day.)
home on the range, For all of your cit - ies so bright,
asked as I gazed, If their glo - ry ex - ceeds that of ours.
cour - ag - ing word, And the skies are not cloud - y all day.
REFRAIN
Home, home on the range, Where the deer and the an - te-lope play, Where
sel -dom is heard a dis - cour- ag-ing word and the skies are not cloud-y all day, (all the day.)

Carry Me Back to Old Virginny

By JAMES A. BLAND
Arr. by George Snowhill

Tenderly
Car-ry me back to old Vir-gin-ny, There's where the cot-ton and the
Car-ry me back to old Vir-gin-ny, There let me live 'till I
corn and 'ta-toes grow, There's where the birds warb-le sweet in the spring-time,
with-er and de-cay, Long by the old Dis-mal Swamp have I wan-der'd,
There's where the old dark-ey's heart am long'd to go. There's where I la-bor'd so
There's where the old dark-ey's life will pass a-way. Mas-sa and mis-sis have
hard for old mas-sa, Day af-ter day in the field of yel-low corn,
long gone be-fore me, Soon we will meet on that bright and gold-en shore,
No place on earth do I love more sin cere ly Than old Vir-gin-ny the state where I was born.
There we'll be hap-py and free from all sor-row, There's where we'll meet and we'll nev-er part no more.

Darling Nelly Gray

Andante

By B. R. HANBY

1. There's a low— green— val - ley on the old Ken-tuck - y shore, Where I've whiled man - y hap - py hours a - way, A - sit - ting and a sing - ing by the lit - tle cot - tage door Where— lived my— darl - ing Nel - ly Gray.
2. When the moon had clim'd the moun - tain and the stars were shin - ing too, Then I'd take my dar - ling Nel - ly Gray, And we'd float down the riv - er in my lit - tle red ca - noe, While my ban - jo— sweet - ly I would play.
CHORUS
O my poor Nel - ly Gray, they have tak - en you a - way, And I'll nev - er see my dar - ling an - y more;— I'm sit - ting by the riv - er and I'm weep - ing all the day, For you've gone from the old Ken tuck - y shore.

Vive la Compagnie

Arr. by A. Fields and F. Hall

With Vigor

Let ev-'ry good fel-low now join in a song, Vi-ve la com-pagn-ie — And
sing to good fel-low-ship loud-ly and long, Vi-ve la com-pagn-ie.
Vi-ve l'a-mour, Vi-ve l'a-mour, Vi-ve l'a-mour, Vi-ve l'a-mour,
Ev-'ry good fel-low now join in the song, Vi-ve la com-pagn-ie. —

It Ain't Gonna Rain No More

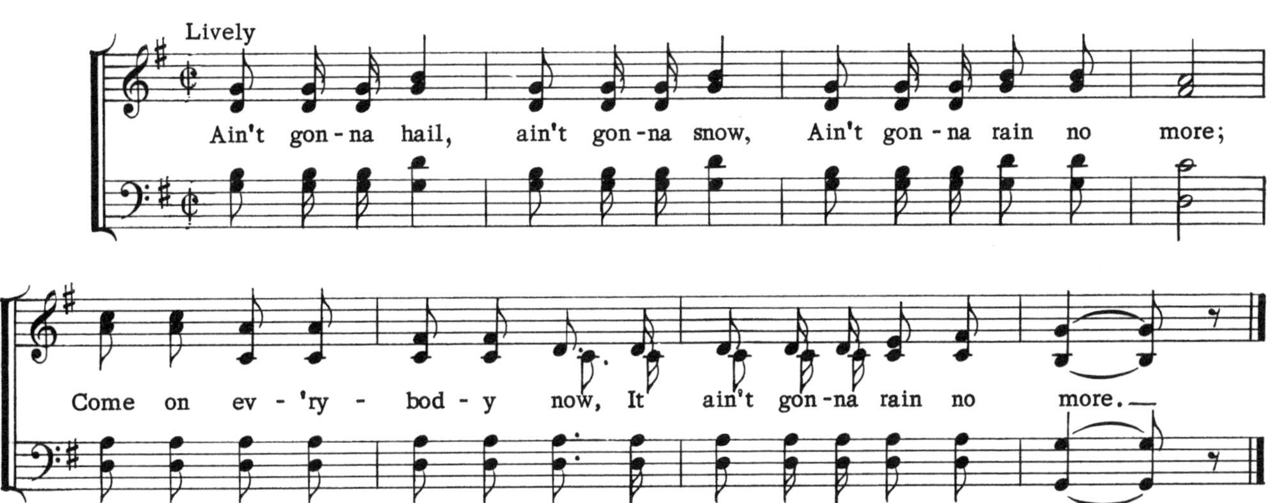
Lively
Ain't gon-na hail, ain't gon-na snow, Ain't gon-na rain no more;
Come on ev-'ry-bod-y now, It ain't gon-na rain no more. —

Old MacDonald Had a Farm

Arr. by
Arthur Fields and Fred Hall

1. Old Mac Don-ald had a farm E - I - E - I - O! And on this farm he
2. Old Mac Don-ald had a farm And on this farm he
had some chicks, E - I - E - I - O! With a chick, chick, here, and a chick, chick there,
had some ducks, With a quack, quack, here, and a quack, quack there,
Here a chick, there a chick, Ev-'ry-where a chick, chick,
Here a quack, there a quack, Ev-'ry-where a quack, quack,
Old MacDonald had a farm E- I- E- I - O!

3. And on this farm he had some turks, E-I-E-I-O!
With a gobble, gobble, here, and a gobble, gobble there,
Here a gobble, there a gobble,
Ev'ry-where a gobble, gobble, etc.

4. And on this farm he had some pigs, E-I-E-I-O!
With a oink, oink, here, and a oink, oink there,
Here a oink, there a oink,
Ev'ry-where a oink, oink, etc.

5. And on this farm he had a Ford, E-I-E-I-O!
With a rattle, rattle, here, and a rattle, rattle there,
Here a rattle, there a rattle,
Ev'ry-where a rattle, etc.

6. And on this farm he had some mules, E-I-E-I-O!
With a he-haw here, and a he-haw there,
Here a he-haw, there a he-haw,
Ev'ry-where a he-haw, etc.

7. And on this farm he had some sheep, E-I-E-I-O!
With a baa, baa, here, and a baa, baa there,
Here a baa baa, there a baa baa,
Ev'ry-where a baa, baa, etc.

8. And on this farm he had some cows, E-I-E-I-O!
With a moo, moo, here, and a moo, moo there,
Here a moo moo, there a moo moo,
Ev'ry-where a moo, moo, etc.

9. And on this farm he had some dogs, E-I-E-I-O!
With a bow-wow here, and a bow-wow there,
Here a bow-wow, there a bow-wow,
Ev'ry-where a bow-wow, etc.

10. And on this farm he had a wife, E-I-E-I-O!
With a gimme, gimme, here and a gimme, gimme there,
Here a gimme, there a gimme,
Ev'ry-where a gimme, gimme, etc.

The Bulldog on the Bank

Moderato
Oh! the bull-dog on the bank! Oh! the bull-dog on the bank:
And the bull-frog in the pool; And the bull-frog in the pool;
Più allegro
Oh! the bull-dog on the bank, And the bull-frog in the pool. The bull-dog call'd the bull-frog A green old wa-ter fool.
Sing-ing tra, la, la, la, la, la, Sing-ing tra, la, la, la, la, -la, Sing-ing tra, la, la, Sing-ing tra, la, la, tra, la, la, la, tra, la, la, la, la, la, la, la, la.
3

2. Says the monkey to the owl,
"Oh, what'll you have to drink?"
"Since you are so very kind,
I'll take a bottle of ink." CHO.

3. Pharaoh's daughter on the bank;
Little Moses in the pool;
She fished him out with a ten-foot pole
And sent him off to school.-CHO.

I Wonder Who's Kissing Her Now

Lyric by
HOUGH & ADAMS

Music by
JOSEPH E. HOWARD
Arr. by Oscar Catsiff

Tempo di valse
mf
I won-der who's kiss-ing her now who's kiss-ing her Won-der who's
teach-ing her how. Won-der who's look-ing in - to her
eyes breath - ing sighs tell - ing lies I
won - der who's buy - ing the wine the wine For lips that I
used to call mine. Won - der if she ev - er
tells him of me I won - der who's kiss - ing her now.

In the Good Old Summer Time

Lyric by REN SHIELDS
Music by GEORGE EVANS
Waltz tempo
sum - mer sum - mer - time
In the good old sum - mer time, In the good old
sum - mer sum - mer - time
sum - mer sum - mer time,
sum - mer time,
Stroll - ing thro' the sha - dy lanes,
sum-mer sum-mer— time
With your ba - by mine; with your ba - by
with your ba - by
You hold her hand and she holds
yours, And that's a ver - y good sign
That she's your
a good sign
toot - sie woot - sie in the good old sum - mer time.

Song of the Islands

Arranged by
JOSEPH WOOD

By
CHAS. E. KING

Slowly and dreamily
Soprano
Alto
Tenor
Bass
mp
(come sopra)
Ha - wai - i, isles of beau - ty, Where skies are
blue and love is true, Where balm - y airs and
gold - en moon light Ca - ress the wav - ing palms of Hon - o -
lu - lu
With more motion, but lightly
pp
mf
Oo Oo Ah Oo
Your val - leys with their rain - bows, Your moun-tains
cresc.
p
Oo Loo loo loo loo Ah - oo
green, the a - zure sea Your fra - grant flow'rs en-

poco rall.
Ah-oo Loo loo loo loo, U-nite and sing a-lo-ha-oe to
poco rall.
chant - ing mu - sic
(come sopra)
Tempo di Valse
pp subito
ften.
me, A - lo - ha - oe to me. When the
cresc. molto
pp subito
Lime flow'r white is gleam-ing And the star-glow
Ah, Ah, Ah,
rit.
a tempo
a-far is stream-ing, Shad-ows fall-ing, your songs are
rit.
a tempo
Ah,
Tempo I°
rit. e dim.
call-ing, to my heart sweet is-land home. Your
rit. e dim.
Is - lands of Ha - wai - i, Where skies of blue are

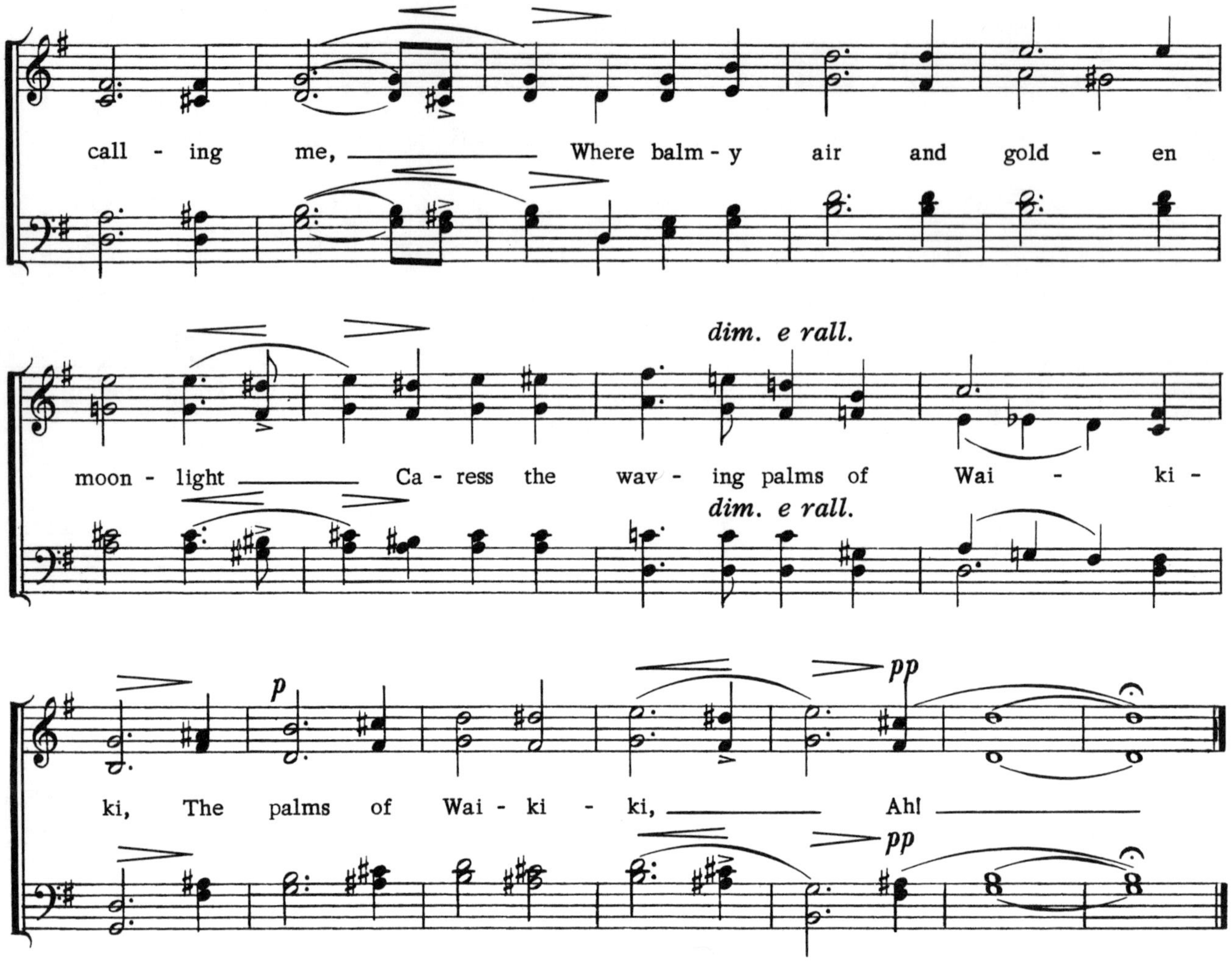

dim. e rall.

call - ing me, ——— Where balm - y air and gold - en moon - light ——— Ca - ress the wav - ing palms of Wai - ki - ki, The palms of Wai - ki - ki, ——— Ah! ———

pp

There'll Be Some Changes Made

Lyric by BILLY HIGGINS and HERBERT EDWARDS

Music by W. BENTON OVERSTREET

Arr. by Oscar Catsiff

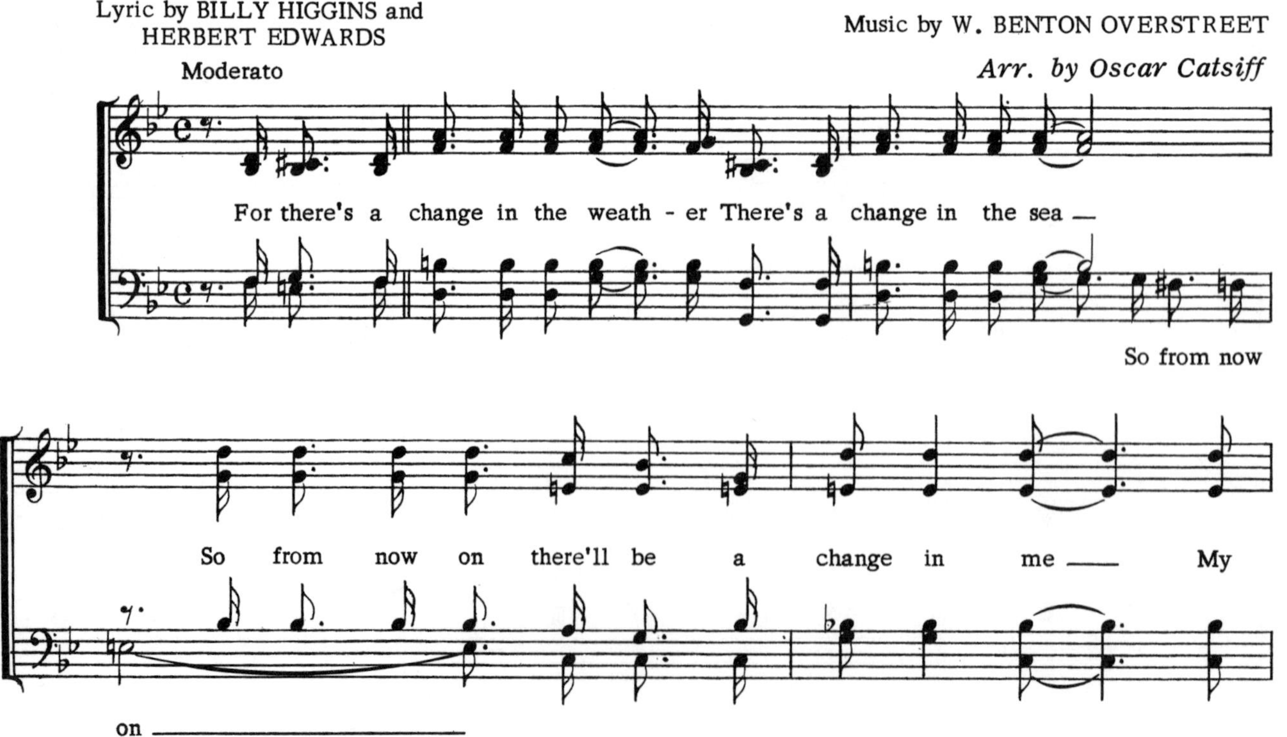
Moderato
For there's a change in the weath - er There's a change in the sea —
So from now
So from now on there'll be a change in me —— My
on ———

walk will be dif - f'rent, my talk and my name
Noth - in' 'bout
I'm goin' to
Noth - in' a - bout me is goin' to be the same
me
change my way of liv - in' if that ain't e - nough
Mm
Then I'll change the way that I strut my stuff
And then I'll
Mm
'Cause No - bod-y wants you when you're
change
old and gray,
There'll be some chang - es
There'll be some chang - es
made to - day
There'll be some chang - es made.
made to day, There'll be some change, be some chang - es made.

She Was Bred in Old Kentucky

HARRY BRAISTED

STANLEY CARTER
Arr. by G. M. Compagno

Andante

She was bred in old Ken - tuck - y, where the mea- dow grass is blue, There's the sun - shine of the coun- try in her face and man -ner too, She was bred in old Ken- tuck- y, take her boy, you're might- y luck- y, When you mar-ry a girl like Sue.(A girl like Sue.)

Turkey in the Straw

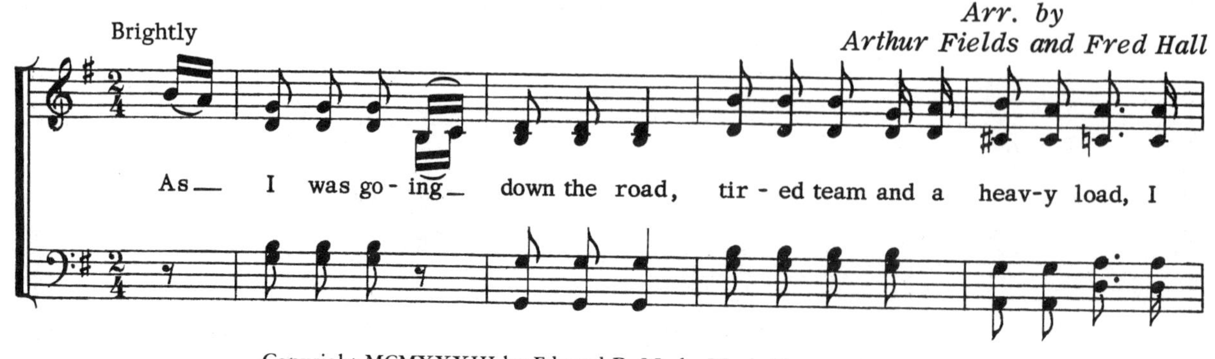
Brightly
Arr. by
Arthur Fields and Fred Hall
As— I was go - ing— down the road, tir - ed team and a heav-y load, I

cracked my whip, and the lead- er sprung;I ___ says "good- bye"_ to the wa -gon tongue.

Tur-key in the straw *(Piano)* Tur-key in the hay *(Piano)*

Roll 'em up twist 'em up a high tuck a haw and_ hit up a tune_ called. Tur-key in the straw.

Sucking Cider Through a Straw

Arr. by
Arthur Fields and Fred Hall
Moderately
1. The pret- tiest girl ___ I ev - er saw ___
2. And now I've got ___ A ma - in law ___
___ Was suck - ing ci - der through a straw. ___
___ From suck - ing ci - der through a straw. ___

The Bear Went Over the Mountain

Arr. by L. Anthony

Moderato
The bear went o - ver the moun - tain, The bear went o - ver the
moun - tain, The bear went o - ver the moun - tain, To see what he could
see. Now all that he could see, Now all that he could
see, Was the oth - er side of the moun - tain, The oth - er side of the
moun- tain, The oth - er side of the moun-tain, Was all that he could see.

Blow, Ye Winds

Allegretto
Arr. by Oscar Catsiff
mf
1. 'Tis ad - ver - tised in Bos - ton, New York and Buf - fa - lo, Five hun - dred brave A - mer - i - cans, a - whal - ing for to go — sing - ing,
2. They send you to New Bed - ford, that fam - ous whal - ing port, And give you to some land - sharks to board and fit you out. — sing - ing,
3. And now we're out to sea, My boys, the wind comes on to blow, One half the watch is sick on deck, the oth - er half be - low, — sing - ing,
Blow, ye winds in the morn - ing, And blow, ye winds, heigh - ho
Clear a - way your run - ning gear, and blow, ye winds, heigh - ho!

The Gal I Left Behind Me

Arranged by
ERNEST GOLD

Lively
(Solo) I struck the trail in sev - en - ty nine, (Chorus)
f
f
The herd strung out be -
f
(Solo)
As I jogged a - long my mind ran back
(Chorus)
hind me.
To the gal I left be -
hind me. That sweet lit - tle gal, that true lit - tle gal, that gal I left be -
hind me. That sweet lit - tle gal, That true lit - tle gal, The gal I left be - hind me.

2. If ever I get off the trail
And Indians don't find me,
I'll make my way straight back again
To the gal I left behind me.

3. The wind did blow, the rain did flow;
The hail did fall and blind me.
I thought of that gal, that sweet little gal,
The gal I left behind me.

4. She wrote ahead to the place I said,
I was always glad to find it,
She says, "I'm true, when you get through,
It's right back here you'll find me."

The Big Rock Candy Mountain

Arr. by L. Anthony

Moderato
On a sun - ny day in the month of May A — Jock - er came a -
hik - ing, He came to a tree and I said to he, "This is just right to my
lik - ing." In the same old month and same old day Then a Hoos - ier's son came
hik - ing, Said the bum to the son," Tell me will you come To the Big Rock Can - dy Moun - tain.
Oh I'll show you the bees and the cig - a - rette trees And the so - da wa - ter
foun - tain And the le - mon - ade springs where the blue - bird sings On the Big Rock Can - dy Moun - tain."

The Quilting Party

Andante
Arr. by Andor Pinter
1. In the sky the bright stars glit - tered, On the bank the pale moon
2. On my arm a soft hand rest - ed, Rest - ed light as o - cean
3. On my lips a whis - per trem - bled, Trem - bled till it dared to
shone; And 'twas
foam; And 'twas from Aunt Di - nah's quilt - ing par - ty, I was see - ing Nel - lie home.
come; And 'twas
cresc.
CHORUS
Tenors
Basses
I was see - ing Nel - lie home, I was see - ing Nel - lie
home; And 'twas from Aunt Di - nah's quilt - ing par - ty, I was see - ing Nel - lie home.

The Old Oaken Bucket

SAMUEL WOODWORTH

Arr. by
Arthur Fields and Fred Hall

Moderato
How dear to my heart are the scenes of my child-hood when fond re - col-lec-tions present them to view. The or - chard, the mea - dow, the deep tan - gled wild-wood and
each lov - ing spot which my in - fan - cy knew. The
REFRAIN
wide spread-ing pond and the
cot of my fath - er, the
mill that stood by it; the bridge and the rock where the cat - a - ract fell. The
lit - tle house nigh it, and too the old buck - et that hung in the well. The
Old Oak - en Buck-et, the i - ron bound buck-et, the moss cov-ered buck-et that hung in the well.

Whoopi Ti-Yi-Yo, Git Along Little Dogies

Arr. by Florence White

In a slow galloping rhythm
As I was a-walk - ing one morn-ing for pleas - ure, I
spied a cow - punch - er come rid - ing a - long. His
hat was throwed back and his spurs was a - jing - ling, and
as he ap - proached he was sing - ing this song.
CHORUS
Whoo - pi Ti - Yi - Yo, git a - long, lit - tle dog - gies, It's

your mis - for - tune and none of my own. Whoo-pi Ti - Yi - Yo git a -
long, lit - tle dog - gies, For you know Wy - o ming will be your new home.

Skip to My Lou

CHORUS
Gaily

Arr. by Florence White

Lou, Lou, Skip to my Lou, Lou, Lou, Skip to my Lou,
Lou, Lou, Skip to my Lou, Skip to my Lou, my dar - ling.

Fine

Lost my part - ner, what'll I do? Lost my part - ner, what'll I do?
Lost my part - ner, what'll I do? Skip to my Lou, my dar - ling.

D. C. al Fine

Down Went McGinty

JOSEPH FLYNN
Arr. by G. M. Compagno

Vigorously
1. Down went Mc-Gin-ty to the bot-tom of the wall, And tho' he won the five, He was more dead than a-live, Sure his ribs, and nose, and back were broke from get-ting such a fall,
2. Down went Mc-Gin-ty to the bot-tom of the hole, Then the driv-er of the cart, Give the load of coal a start, And it took us half an hour to dig Mc-Gin-ty from the coal,
3. Down went Mc-Gin-ty to the bot-tom of the jail, Where his board would cost him nix, And he stay'd ex-act-ly six, They were big long months he stopp'd for no one went his bail,
4. Down went Mc-Gin-ty to the bot-tom of the bay, And he must be ve-ry wet, For they have-n't found him yet, But they say his ghost comes round the docks be-fore the break of day,
Dress'd in his best suit of clothes.
Oh! Oh!

Upidee

Allegretto.
mf
1. The shades of night were fall - ing fast, Tra, la, la, Tra, la, la, As
2. His brow was sad, his eye be - neath, Tra, la, la, Tra. la, la, Flash'd
3. "Oh stay," the maid - en said, "and rest Tra, la, la, Tra, la, la, Thy
thro' an Al-pine vil-lage passed, Tra la, la, la, la! A youth, who bore, 'mid snow and ice, A
like a fal - chion from its sheath, Tra la, la, la, la! And like a sil - ver clar-ion, rung The
wea- ry head up - on this breast!" Tra la, la, la, la! A tear stood in his bright blue eye, But
ritard.
ban-ner with the strange de - vise:
ac -cents of that un- known tongue: U-pi - dee-i, dee-i, da, U- pi -dee, U- pi- da,
still he an - swered with a sigh:
U- pi-dee-i, dee-i - da, U-pi - dee-i da!
(Imitating a watchman's rattle.)
r-r-r-r-r-r-r-r-r-r-r-r yah! yah! yah! yah!
U-pi-dee-i-dee- i -da, U-pi-dee, U-pi- da, U- pi-dee-i, dee-i- da, U-pi -dee-i-da!

Rule Britannia

JAMES THOMSON

THOMAS ARNE
Arr. by G.M. Compagno

Majestically
1. When Brit - ain first at Heav'n's com - mand A-
2. The na - tions not so blest as thee, Must
3. Still more ma jes - tic shalt thou rise, More
4. Thee haugh - ty ty - rants ne'er shall tame; All
5. To thee be - longs the rur - al reign, Thy
6. The mu - ses, still with free - dom found, Shall
rose from out the a - zure main, A - rose from out the
in their turn to ty - rants fall, Must in their turn to
dread - ful from each for - eign stroke, More dread - ful from each
their at - tempts to bend thee down. All their at - tempts to
cit - ies shall with com - merce shine, Thy cit - ies shall with
to thy hap - py coast re - pair, Shall to thy hap - py
a - zure main, the a - zure main; This was the char - ter, the
ty - rants fall, to ty - rants fall; Whilst thou shalt flour - ish, shall
for - eigh stroke, each for - eign stroke. As the loud blasts that tear
bend thee down, to bend thee down, Will but a rouse thy gen-
com - merce shine, with com - merce shine. All thine shall be the sub-
coast re - pair, thy coast re - pair, Blessed Isle with match-less beau-
char - ter of the land, And guard - ian an - gels sang this strain:
flour - ish great and free, The dread and en - vy of them all.
thy skies, tear thy skies, Serve but to root thy na - tive oak.
'rous flame, gen - 'rous flame To work their woe but thy re - nown.
ject main, sub - ject main, And ev - 'ry shore in cir - cle thine.
ty, with beau - ty crowned, And man ly hearts to guard the fair.

Rule, Bri- tan- nia, Bri - tan -nia rule the waves! Bri- tons nev - er shall be slaves.

The Wraggle Taggle Gypsies, O!

Moderato

Arr. by George Snowhill

1. There were three gyp - sies a — come to my door, and
2. Then — she pulled off her — silk fin - ished gown and
3. It was late last night, when my lord came — home in-

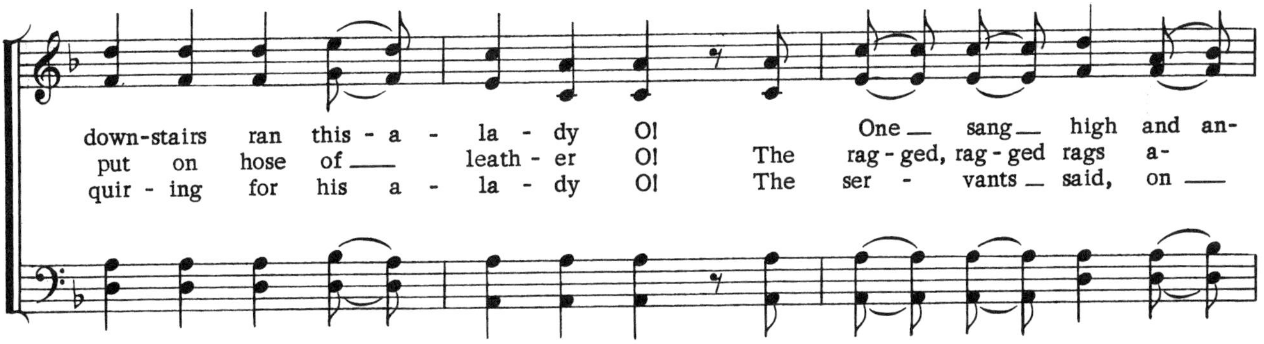

down-stairs ran this - a - la - dy O! One — sang — high and an-
put on hose of — leath - er O! The rag - ged, rag - ged rags a-
quir - ing for his a - la - dy O! The ser - vants — said, on —

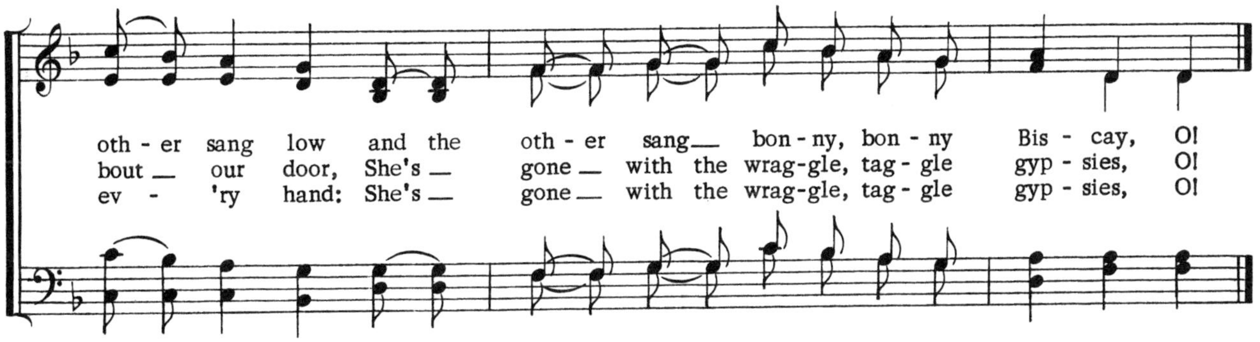

oth - er sang low and the oth - er sang — bon - ny, bon - ny Bis - cay, O!
bout — our door, She's — gone — with the wrag-gle, tag - gle gyp - sies, O!
ev - 'ry hand: She's — gone — with the wrag-gle, tag - gle gyp - sies, O!

La Marseillaise

ROUGET DE LISLE
Arr. by G. M. Compagno
Majestically
Ye sons of France a - wake to glo - ry! Hark! Hark! what my - riads bid you
Al-lons, en - fants de la pa - tri - e! Le jour de gloire est ar -ri-
rise! Your child- ren, wives, and grand-sires_ hoar-y, Be-hold their tears, and hear their
vé! Con- tre nous de la ty - ran - ni- e L'é-ten-dard san-glant est le -
cries! Be- hold their tears, and_hear their_ cries! Shall hate- ful ty - rants, mis-chief
vé! L'é-ten-dard san-glant est le - vé! En-ten-dez - vous, dans les cam -
breed-ing With hire-ling hosts, a ruf - fian_ band, Af - fright and des - o - late the
pa - gnes, Mu -gir ces fé - ro-ces sol - dats? Ils vien- nent jusque dans nos
land;_ When_ peace and lib-er - ty lie bleed-ing? To arms, to arms ye
bras_ E - gor -ger nos fils, nos cam - pa- gnes! Aux ar - mes, ci- to-

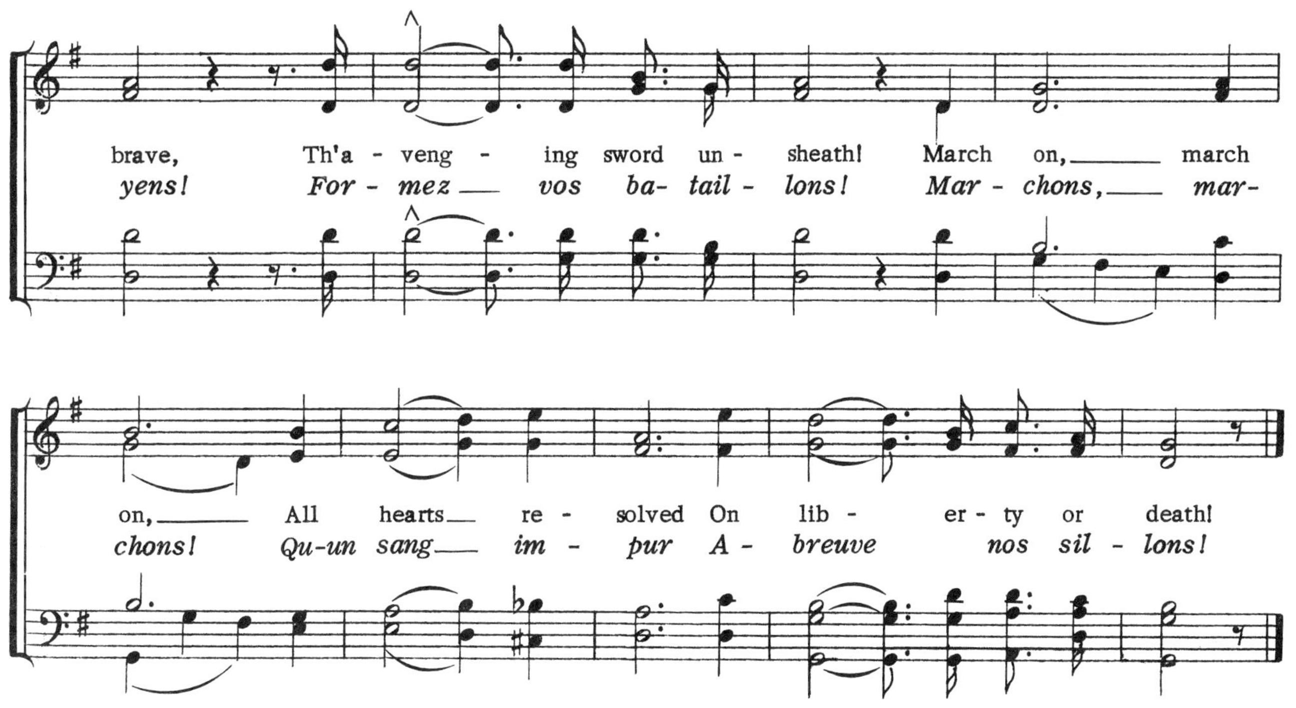
brave, Th'a - veng - ing sword un - sheath! March on, march
yens! For - mez vos ba- tail - lons! Mar - chons, mar-
on, All hearts re - solved On lib - er - ty or death!
chons! Qu-un sang im - pur A - breuve nos sil - lons!

Du, Du, Liegst Mir im Herzen

English Version by
DON TITMAN

Arr. by G. M. Compagno

Moderato

You, you ten - der and wist - ful, You, you haunt all my dreams
Du, du, liegst mir im Her - zen, Du, du, liegst mir im Sinn,

Lov - ing you would be bliss - ful, But you care noth - ing, it
Du, du, machst mir viel Schmer - zen, Weisst nicht wie gut ich dir

seems. Oh, you care not, But you care noth- ing, it seems.
bin. Du, du, du, du, Weisst nicht wie gut ich dir bin.

O Canada

French Text by
ADOLPHE B. ROUTHIER
Maestoso
C. LAVALLÉE
Arranged by Felix Guenther
p
O Can - a - da, Your roll - ing prai - ries call Far o'er the world To cheer us, one and all; For you shall breed great hearts to lead Your noble des - ti - ny, Till all ac-claim with might and main Dear Can - a - da, the free!
O Can - a - da, By na - ture rich en - dow'd, Glad - ly we join To sing your prais - es loud; By mount and glen, strong stead - fast men Full well your cause shall serve, That in the gold - en days to come Your gifts they may de - serve.
O Can - a - da! Ter - re de nos aï - eux, Ton front est ceint de fleu - rons glo - ri - eux! Car ton bras sait por - ter l'é - pé - e, Il sait por - ter la croix! Ton his - toire est une é - po - pé - e Des plus bril-lants ex - ploits.
cresc.
CHORUS
f
O Can - a - da, Fair Can - a - da, Wide are your a - cres flung from sea to sea, Hail Can - a - da, great land of lib - er - ty!
Et ta va - leur, de foi trem - pée, Pro - té - ge - ra nos foy - ers et nos droits, Pro - té - ge - ra nos foy-ers et nos droits.

The Maple Leaf Forever

Not too slow
A. MUIR
Arr. by George Snowhill
1. In days of yore, from Brit-ain's shore, Wolfe, the daunt-less he - ro came and plant - ed firm Bri - tan - nia's flag on Ca - na - da's fair do - main; Here may it wave, our boast, our pride, and joined in love to - geth-er, The This - tle, Sham - rock, Rose en - twine the Ma - ple Leaf for - ev - er.
2. At Queen-ston Heights and Lun - dy's Lane, our brave fath - ers side by side, for free - dom, homes, and loved ones dear firm - ly stood and nob - ly died; And those dear rights which they main - tained, we swear to yield them nev-er, Our watch - word ev - er more shall be, the Ma - ple Leaf for - ev - er.
CHORUS
The Ma - ple Leaf our em - blem dear, The Ma - ple Leaf for - ev - er, God save our Queen and Hea - ven bless The Ma - ple Leaf for - ev - er.

Men of Harlech

Welsh National Song
Arr. by G. M. Compagno

With dignity
mf
1. Men — of Har - lech in the hol-low Do ye hear, like rush - ing bil - low,
2. Rock - y steeps — and pass-es nar-row Flash with spear and flight of ar - row,
Wave — on wave — that surg - ing fol - low Bat - tles — dis - tant sound?
Who — would think — of death or sor - row? Death is — glo - ry now!
'Tis — the tramp — of Sax - on foe - men, Sax - on spear-men, Sax - on bow - men
Hurl — the reel - ing horse-men ov - er, Let the earth dead foe-men cov - er,
Be — they Knights, — or hinds or yeo-men, They — shall bite — the ground!
Fate — of friend — or wife or lov - er Trem - bles on — a blow.
Loose — the folds — a - sun - der, Flag — we con - quer un - der, The
Strands — of life — are riv - en, Blow — for blow — is giv - en, In

plac - id sky now bright on high Shall launch its bolts of thun-der!
dead - ly lock or bat - tle shock, And mer - cy shrieks to heav - en!

ff
On - ward! 'tis our coun - try needs us; He is brav-est, he who leads us!
Men of Har - lech! young or hoar - y, Would you win a name in sto - ry,

Hon - or's self now proud - ly heads us! Free - dom! God and Right!
Strike for home, for life, for glo - ry, Free - dom! God and Right!

Where, Oh Where, Has My Little Dog Gone?

(ZU LAUTERBACH)

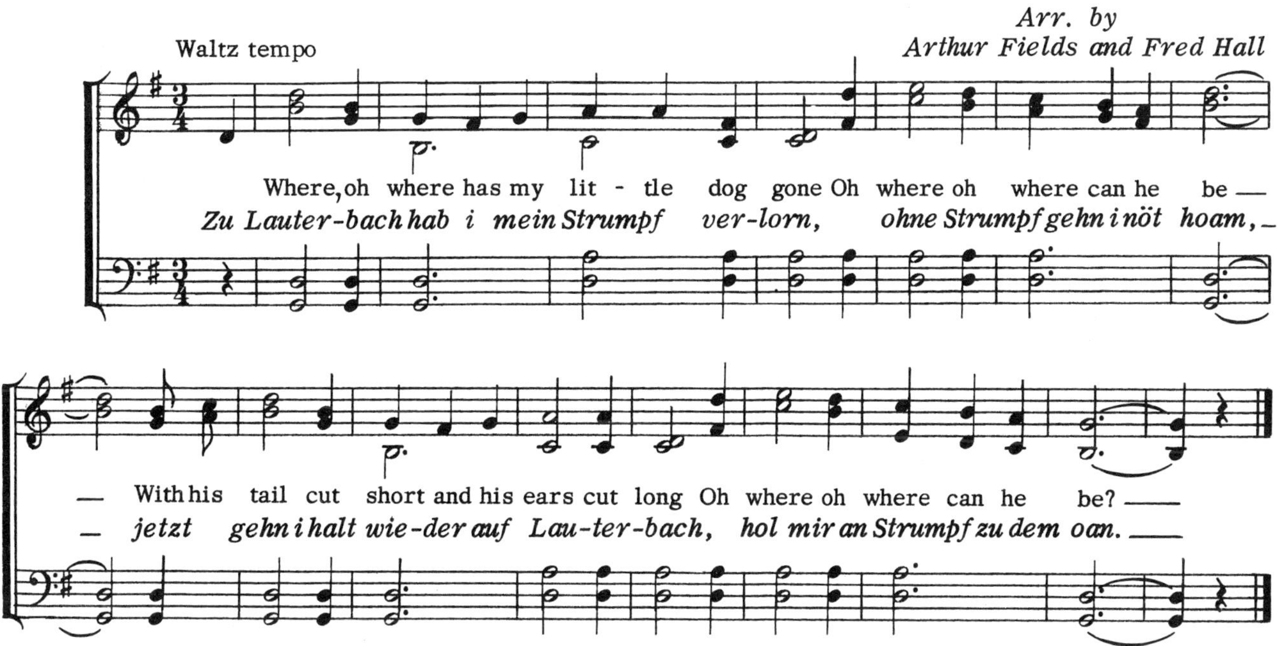
Arr. by
Arthur Fields and Fred Hall
Waltz tempo
Where, oh where has my lit - tle dog gone Oh where oh where can he be
Zu Lauter-bach hab i mein Strumpf ver-lorn, ohne Strumpf gehn i nöt hoam,
With his tail cut short and his ears cut long Oh where oh where can he be?
jetzt gehn i halt wie-der auf Lau-ter-bach, hol mir an Strumpf zu dem oan.

Come Back to Erin

CLARIBEL
Arr. by G. M. Compagno

Slowly, with expression.
Come back to E - rin Ma - vour - neen, Ma -vour -neen, Come back a-roon, to the
land of thy birth; Come with the sham- rocks and Spring- time, Ma-vour- neen,
And its Kil- lar - ney, shall ring with our mirth. Sure when we lent ye to
beau - ti - ful Eng - land, Lit - tle we thought of the lone win - ter days,
Lit - tle we thought of the hush of the star shine O - ver the moun-tain, the
bluffs and the brays! Then come back to E - rin, Ma - vour - neen, Ma - vour- neen,

Come back a - gain to the land of thy birth. — Come back to E - rin, Ma -
vour- neen, Ma - vour- neen, And its Kil - lar - ney shall ring with our mirth.

Kathleen Mavourneen

JULIA CRAWFORD

FREDERICK CROUCH
Arr. by G. M. Groene

Moderately slow

mf

1. Kath - leen Ma - vour - neen! the grey dawn is break- ing, — The horn of the hun- ter is — heard — on the hill; The lark from her light wing the bright dew is shak - ing, — Kath- leen — Ma - vour-neen! what slum-bring still!
2. Kath - leen Ma - vour - neen! a - wake from thy slum -bers; — The blue moun-tains glow in the — sun's gold-en light; Ah! where is the spell that once hung on my num - bers? A - rise — in thy beau-ty, thou star of my night.

Oh, hast thou for - got - ten how soon we must sev - er? Oh,
Ma - vour - neen, Ma - vour - neen, my sad tears are fall - ing, To
hast thou for - got - ten this day we must part? It may be for
think that from E - rin and thee I must part! It may be for
years, and it may be for - ev - er; Oh, why art thou si - lent, thou
years, and it may be for - ev - er; Then why art thou si - lent, thou
voice of my heart? It may be for years, and it may be for -
voice of my heart? It may be for years, and it may be for -
ev - er; Then why art thou si - lent, Kath - leen Ma - vour - neen?
ev - er; Then why art thou si - lent, Kath - leen Ma - vour - neen?

Auld Lang Syne
Robert Burns
Old Scotch Air
Arr. by G. M. Groene
With sentiment
1. Should auld ac-quaint-ance be for-got, And nev - er brought to mind? Should auld ac-quaint-ance be for-got And_ days of Auld Lang Syne?
2. And here's a hand my trus - ty frien', And gie's a hand o' thine; We'll tak' a cup o' kind - ness yet,_____ for___ Auld Lang Syne.
REFRAIN
For Auld__ Lang__ Syne, my dear, For Auld__ Lang__ Syne, We'll tak' a cup o' kind ness yet, For__ Auld__ Lang__ Syne.
Stars of the Summer Night
mp Dolce.
1. Stars of the sum - mer night, Far in yon az - ure deeps, Hide, hide your gold -en light, She sleeps, my la - dy sleeps; She sleeps, she sleeps, my la - dy sleeps.
2. Moon of the sum - mer night, Far down yon west - ern steeps, Sink, sink in sil - ver light, She sleeps, my la - dy sleeps; She sleeps, she sleeps, my la - dy sleeps.
rall.

The Harp that Once thro' Tara's Halls

THOMAS MOORE

Air "Gramachree"
Arr. by G. M. Compagno

Slowly, with dignity.

1. The harp that once thro' Ta - ra's halls, The soul of mu - sic shed; Now
2. No more to chiefs and la - dies bright, The harp of Ta - ra swells; The

hangs as mute on Ta - ra's walls As if that soul were fled: So
chord, a - lone, that breaks at night, Its tale of ru - in tells: Thus

sleeps the pride of form - er days, So glo - ry's thrill is o'er, And
free - dom now so sel - dom wakes The on - ly throb she gives, Is

hearts that once beat high for praise, Now feel that pulse no more.
when some heart in - dig - nant breaks, To show that still she lives.

Au Clair de la Lune

J. B. LULLY

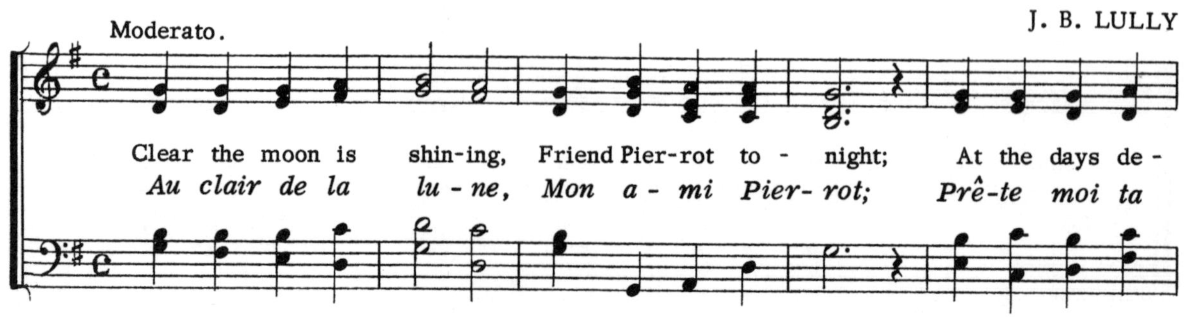
Moderato.
Clear the moon is shin-ing, Friend Pier-rot to - night; At the days de -
Au clair de la lu - ne, Mon a - mi Pier- rot; Prê-te moi ta

cli - ning, I've no fire nor light. Pen and pa - per lend me, Just one word to
plu - me pour e' - crire un mot. Ma chan-delle est mor - te Je n'ai plus de
write, Pray you, do not send me, From your door this night.
feu; Ou - vre moi ta por - te, Pour l'a- mour de Dieu.

The Soldiers' Farewell

(HOW CAN I LEAVE THEE?)

Music by JOHANNA KINKEL

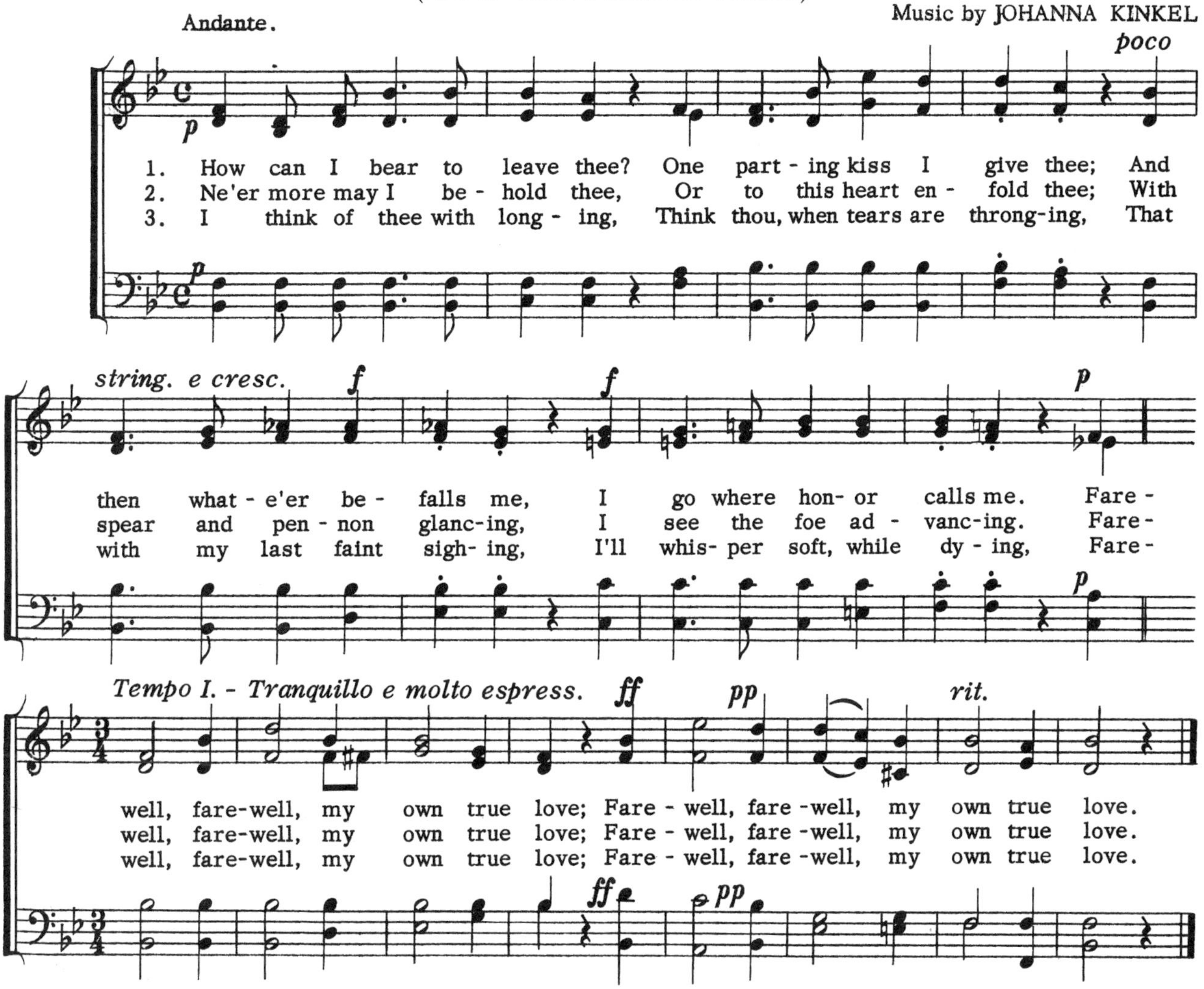

Andante.

p *poco*

1. How can I bear to leave thee? One part - ing kiss I give thee; And
2. Ne'er more may I be - hold thee, Or to this heart en - fold thee; With
3. I think of thee with long - ing, Think thou, when tears are throng-ing, That

string. e cresc. *f* *f* *p*

then what - e'er be - falls me, I go where hon- or calls me. Fare -
spear and pen - non glanc-ing, I see the foe ad - vanc-ing. Fare -
with my last faint sigh- ing, I'll whis- per soft, while dy - ing, Fare -

Tempo I. - Tranquillo e molto espress. *ff* *pp* *rit.*

well, fare-well, my own true love; Fare - well, fare -well, my own true love.
well, fare-well, my own true love; Fare - well, fare -well, my own true love.
well, fare-well, my own true love; Fare - well, fare -well, my own true love.

Londonderry Air

Slowly, with expression.
Arr. by G. M. Compagno
Would God I were the ten-der ap-ple blos- - som that floats and
falls from off the twist-ed bough,— To lie and faint with-in your silk-en
bos - om With-in your silk-en bos - om as that does
now!— Or would I were a lit-tle bur-nish'd ap - ple, For you to
pluck me glid-ing by so cold;— While sun and shade your robe of lawn will
dap - ple your robe of lawn and your hair's spun gold.—

The Wearing of the Green

Arr. by
Arthur Fields and Fred Hall

Allegretto
Oh Pad-dy dear and did you hear the news that's go-in' 'round The
Saint Pat-rick's day no more we'll keep his col-or can't be seen For
sham-rock is for-bid-den for to grow on I-rish ground.
there's a blood-y law a-gin the wear-in' of the green.
I met with Nap-per Tan-dy And he took me by the hand And he
said "How's poor old Ire-land and how does she stand?" She's the
most dis-tress-ful coun-try, sir, that ev-er you have seen They're
hang-ing men and wo-men For the wear-ing of the green.

The Minstrel Boy

THOMAS MOORE

Air:-"THE MOREEN"
Arr. by G. M. Compagno

With spirit
1. The min-strel boy to the war is gone, in the ranks of death you'll find him; His fath - er's sword he has gird - ed on, And his wild harp slung be - hind him. "Land of Song!" said the war-rior bard "Tho' all the world be - trays thee, One sword, at least, thy rights shall guard, One faith - ful harp shall praise thee!"
2. The min-strel fell, but the foe-man's chain, Could not bring that proud soul un - der; The harp he loved ne'er spoke a - gain, For he tore its chords a - sun - der, And said, "No chain shall sul - ly thee, Thou soul of love and brav - 'ry! Thy songs were made for the pure and free, They shall nev - er sound in slav - 'ry."

Killarney

MICHAEL BALFE
Arr. by G. M. Compagno

Moderately.
1. By Kil - lar - ney's — lakes and fells, Em - 'rald isles and — wind - ing bays,
2. In - nis - fal - len's — ru - ined shrine, May sug - gest a — pass - ing sigh,
Moun - tain paths and — wood - land dells Mem - 'ry ev - er fond - ly strays.
But man's faith can — ne'er de - cline, Such God's won - ders float - ing by.
Boun - teous na - ture loves all lands, Beau - ty wan - ders ev - 'ry - where,
Cas - tle Lough and Gle - na bay, Moun - tains Tore and Ea - gle's Nest,
Foot - prints leave on man - y strands, — But her home is — sure - ly there!
Still at Muck-cross you must pray, — Tho' the monks are — now at rest.
An - gels fold their wings and rest, In that E - den of the west,
An - gels won - der not that man, There would fain pro - long life's span,
Beau - ty's home Kil - lar - ney, Ev - er fair — Kil - lar - ney.
Beau - ty's home Kil - lar - ney, Ev - er fair — Kil - lar - ney.

The Campbells Are Comin'

Scotch Air
Arr. by G. M. Groene
Lively
The Camp-bells are com-in', O ho, O ho, The Camp-bells are com-in' O ho, O ho, The Camp-bells are com-in' to bon-nie Loch-lev-en, The Camp-bells are com-in' O ho, O ho,
Fine
Up-on the Lo-monds I lay, I lay, Up-on the Lo-monds I lay, I lay, I look-ed down to bon-nie Loch-lev-en And heard three bon-nie pi-pers play The
The great Ar-gyle he goes be-fore, He makes his can-non loud-ly roar; Wi' sound of trum-pet, pipe, and drum, The Camp-bells are com-in' O ho! O ho! The
D. S.

The Blue Bells of Scotland

(WHERE HAS MY HIGHLAND LADDIE GONE?)

Traditional
Arr. by G. M. Compagno

Moderately
1. O where, and O where is your High-land lad-die gone? O
2. O where, and O where does your High-land lad-die dwell? O -
3. Sup - pose, and sup - pose that your High-land lad should die? Sup -
where, and O where is your High-land lad - die gone?
where, and O where does your High-land lad - die dwell?
pose, and sup - pose that your High-land lad should die?
He's gone to fight the foe, for King George up - on the throne; And it's
He dwelt in mer - ry Scot - land at the sign of the Blue Bell; And it's
The bag - pipes shall play o'er him, and I'd lay me down and cry; But it's
oh! in my heart, how I wish him safe at home.
oh! in my heart, that I love my lad - die well.
oh! in my heart, that I wish he may not die.

Robin Adair

Arr. by George Snowhill

Andante
1. What's this dull town to me? Ro - bin's not near. What was't I wished to see? What wish'd to hear? Where's all the joy and mirth made this town a heav'n on earth? Oh! they're all fled with thee, Ro - bin A - dair.
2. What made th'as - sem - bly shine? Ro - bin A- dair What made the ball so fine? Ro - bin A- dair What, when the play was o'er, what made my heart so sore? Oh! it was part - ing with Ro - bin A - dair.

Annie Laurie

WILLIAM DOUGLASS

LADY JOHN SCOTT

Moderately
Max - wel - ton's braes are bon - nie, Where ear - ly falls the
Her brow is like the snow - drift, Her throat is like the
dew, And twas there that An - nie Lau - rie Gave
swan; Her face it is the fair - est That
me her prom - ise true; Gave me her prom - ise
e'er the sun shone on; That e'er the sun shone
true, Which ne'er for - got will be,
on; And dark blue is her e'e,
And for
bon - nie An - nie Lau - rie, I'd lay me down and dee.

Cockles and Mussels

Simply, with tenderness
mp
Arr. by George Snowhill
1. In Dub - lin's fair cit - y where girls are so pret - ty, 'Twas
2. She was a fish - mon - ger, but that was no won - der; Her
3. She died of the "fa - ver" and no one could save her, Sure,
there that I met with sweet Mol - ly Ma - lone; She— drove a wheel-bar - row through
fa - ther and moth - er were fish - mon - gers too. They— drove their wheel-bar - row through
that's how I lost my sweet Mol - ly Ma - lone. Now her ghost drives her bar - row through
rit.
mf 1st time: sweetly
f 2nd time: cackling
p 3rd time: gently
streets old and nar - row
streets old and nar - row
streets old and nar - row
Cry - ing: "Cock - les and mus - sels, a - live, a - live, O!"
a tempo
same as above
A - live, a-live, O, — A - live, a-live, O, — Cry-ing: "Cock-les and mus-sels a - live, a-live, O!"

Bendemeer's Stream

Words by THOMAS MOORE

Arr. by George Snowhill

Slowly
There's a bow - er of ros - es by Ben - de - meer's stream, and the
time of my child-hood 'twas like a sweet dream, to —
night - in - gale sings 'round it all the day long, In the
sit in the ros - es and hear the birds' song. That —
bow'r and its mus - ic I nev - er for - get, but oft when a -
lone, in the bloom of the year, I think: "Is the night - in - gale
sing- ing there— yet? Are the ros - es still bright by the calm Ben-de - meer?

My Bonnie

Scotch Air
Arr. by G. M. Groene

Waltz time
My Bonnie lies over the ocean, My Bonnie lies over the sea; My Bonnie lies over the ocean, Oh, bring back my Bonnie to me.
Last night as I lay on my pillow, Last night as I lay on my bed; Last night as I lay on my pillow, I dreamt that my Bonnie was dead.
Oh, blow, ye winds, over the ocean, And blow ye winds over the sea; Oh, blow, ye winds over the ocean And bring back my Bonnie to me.
The winds have blown over the ocean, The winds have blown over the sea; The winds have blown over the ocean And brought back my Bonnie to me, back to me.
CHORUS
Bring back, bring back, bring back my Bonnie to me, to me;
rall.
Bring back, bring back, Oh! bring back my Bonnie to me.

Loch Lomond

Words by LADY JOHN SCOTT
Marching time
1. By yon bon-nie banks an' yon bon-nie braes, The sun shines bright on Loch
2. 'Twas there that we part ed in yon shad - y glen, On the steep, steep side o' Loch
Lo - mond, Where me and my true love were ev - er wont to gae, On the
Lo - mond, Where pur - ple in hue, the High-land hills we view, An' the
bon-nie, bon-nie banks o' Loch Lo - mond. O ye'll take the high road, an'
moon com-in' out in the gloam - in'. O ye'll take the high road, an'
I'll take the low road, An' I'll be in Scot-land a - fore ye, For
I'll take the low road, An' I'll be in Scot-land a - fore ye, For
me an' my true love will ne-ver meet a-gain On the bon-nie, bon-nie banks o' Loch Lo - mond.
me an' my true love will ne-ver meet a-gain On the bon-nie, bon-nie banks o' Loch Lo - mond.

La Spagnola

English Words by
F. A. GROENE
VINCENZO DI CHIARA
Arr. by G. M. Compagno
Moderate Waltz-time.
mf
La Spag - no - la Beau - ti - ful maid of
Stret - ti, stret - ti nel - l'e- sta - si d'a-
Spain. Ah! how of - ten I dream of thee,
mor! La Spa - gno - la sa a - mar co - si,
Hum - ming soft - ly this mel - o - dy. Sing - ing,
boc - ca e boc -ca la not - te eil di. Stret - ti,
Danc - ing, love - ly maid of Spain. Al - ways
stret - ti nel-l'e sta - si d'a - mor! La Spa-
of Spain.
d'a - mor!
Optional Ending
dear, will your mem - 'ry be, Oh! tell me you think of me.
gno -la sa a - mar co - si boc - ca e boc -ca la not - te eildi.

Aloha Oe

By H. M. QUEEN LILIUOKALANI

Moderato
Proud - ly swept the rain - cloud by the cliff As
Ha - a - heo ka u - a i - na pa - li Ke
on it glid - ed thro' the trees Still fol - low - ing with grief the
nihi a - e - la ka - na - he - le E ha - ha - i a - na i - ka
li - ko The a - hi - hi - le - hua of the vale
li - ko Pu - a a - hi - hi - le - hu - a o u - ka
ff
Fare - well to thee, fare - well to thee Thou charm - ing one who dwells a - mong the
A - lo - ha oe a - lo - ha oe E ke o - na - o - na no - ho i - ka
bow - 'rs One fond em - brace be - fore I now de - part Un - til we meet a - gain.
li - po One fond em - brace a ho - i a - e au Un - til we meet a - gain.

La Cucaracha

English Words by
STANLEY ADAMS
Arr. by G. M. Compagno
Lively
1. La Cu - ca - ra - cha, La Cu - ca - ra - cha, Run -ning up and down the
2. La Cu - ca - ra - cha, La Cu - ca - ra - cha, Wan-dered in a dress- ing
3. La Cu - ca - ra - cha, La Cu - ca - ra - cha, Met a lit -tle Pek - ing -
4. La Cu - ca - ra - cha, La Cu - ca - ra - cha, Woke up on e - lec - tion
La Cu - ca - ra - cha, La Cu - ca - ra - cha, Ya no pue de ca - mi -
house, La Cu - ca - ra - cha, La Cu - ca - ra - cha, Qui - et as a lit - tle
room, A love -ly la - dy, A pret - ty la - dy, Could -n't see well in the
ese, La Cu - ca - ra - cha, La Cu - ca - ra - cha, Bit his nose and made him
day, La Cu - ca - ra - cha, La Cu - ca - ra - cha, Heard the things they had to
nar, Por que no tie - ne, por que le fal - ta, Ma-ri - hua - na que fu-
mouse, He gets in trou - ble, A lot of trou - ble, Snoop-ing here and ev - 'ry -
gloom, La -Cu - ca - ra - cha, La Cu - ca - ra - cha, Fell in - to her make-up
sneeze, The lit- -tle dog - gie, The lit - tle dog - gie, Tho' he dug and dug and
say, A lot of ly - ing, and a - li - bi - ing, Emp - ty heads with-out a
mar, La Cu - ca - ra - cha, La Cu - ca - ra - cha, Ya no pue-de ca - mi -
where, La Cu - ca ra - cha, La Cu - ca - ra - cha, Al - ways keeps the cup-board
bowl, When she had paint - ed, she near -ly faint - ed, Though her face had grown a
dug, La Cu - ca ra - cha, La Cu - ca - ra - cha, He was safe be -neath a
plan, La Cu - ca ra - cha, La Cu - ca - ra - cha, Said, "I'm glad I'm not a
nar, Por que no tie - ne por que le fal - ta Ma - ri - hua- na que fu -

bare. Then one day when cook was bak - ing, Won-dered he "What is she
mole. Lat - er on when he was old - er, Then he found the nights much
rug. Then one day when he was thin - ner, He just looked a - round for
man." Then one day he saw an ar - my, Said, "The drums and bu - gle
mar. Un pan a de ro fue a - mi - sa, No en con-tran- do que re -
mak - ing?" For it looked so ap - pe - tiz - ing, With the bat - ter slow -ly
cold - er, 'Till he saw a sleeve wide o - pen, Snug and warm as he was
din - ner, And he tumb-led nev - er think -ing, In the soup and start - ed
charm me, Still if all the world are broth - ers, Why should these men fight the
zar. Le pi-di -o a-la Vir-gen pu - ra, Di- ne - ro pa - ra gas-
ris - ing, To the edge he start - ed skip - ping,
hop - in', 'Twas the time and place for nap - ping,
sink - ing, Oh the cook be - gan to hol - ler,
oth - ers? Guess it's just for love and glo - ry,
tar; Un pan a de - ro fue a - mi - sa,
Then he found that he was slip - ping, In the pie so hot and
'Till some - bo - dy start - ed slap - ping, Woe be - tide the lit - tle
Grabbed the but - ler by the col - lar, Out the win - dow went the
Who'd be - lieve an - oth - er sto - ry? These are men so brave and
No en con - tran - do que - re - zar; Le pi de - o a la Vir- gen
D. S. al Fine Fine.
blaz - in', Now he's just an - oth - er rais - in. La Cu - ca - rais - in.
mid - get, He had made the own- er fidg -et. La Cu - ca - fid - get.
plat - ter, But our lit - tle friend was fat - ter. La Cu - ca - fat - ter.
pluck - y, Look at me, boy am I luck - y." La Cu - ca - luck - y."
pu - ra, Di - ne - ro pa - ra gas - tar. La Cu - ca- tar.

CODA
La Cu-ca - ra - cha La Cu-ca - ra - cha, Just the same as you and
I, He got the jit. - ters, the sweets and bit - ters, Lived and loved and said "Good - bye."

Ach Du Lieber Augustin

English Version by
DON TITMAN

Arr. by G. M. Compagno

Brightly.

Ach du lie - ber Au - gu -stin, Au - gu -stin, Au - gu -stin, Ach du lie- ber
Ach du lie - ber Au - gu-stin Au - gu-stin Au - gu -stin, Ach du lie -ber

Au - gu - stin, Ev - 'ry - thing's gone! Pock- ets are emp - ty, The
Au - gu - stin Al- les ist hin; s'Geld is weg s'Mad-'lis hin,

wife she has left me, still we will keep on sing- ing Though ev-'ry thing's wrong.
alles is weg Au - gu - stin;Ach du lie -ber Au - gu - stin al - les ist hin.

The Loreley

Arr. by Andor Pinter

Andante moderato.
p
1. I know not what it pre - sa - ges, That I am so sad to - day; A
2. The most beau-ti-ful maid is re - clin-ing On the cliff so won - drous fair; Her
3. It seiz-es with wild - est yearn-ing The boat- man, en-tranc'd in his skiff; He
leg- end of for - mer a - ges Will not from my thoughts a - way The
glo - ri-ous jew - els are shin - ing, She is comb- ing her gold - en hair; With a
sees not the trea-cher-ous break-ers, He gaz - es a - lone on the cliff. And
mf
cresc.
air is cool and it dar - kens, The Rhine flows calm - ly on The
gold - en comb she combs it, And sings a song there - by, That
soon will the waves en - gulf them, Both boat and boat - man strong, For
peak of the mount - ain spar - kles In the glow of the eve - ning sun
thrills with its mys - tic mean - ing And pow-er - ful mel - o - dy.
thus in her toils hath she bound them, The Lo - re - ley with her song.

Home, Sweet Home

JOHN HOWARD PAYNE
Andante sostenuto
HENRY BISHOP
p
1. Mid pleas-ures and pal - a - ces though we may roam, Be it ev - er so
2. I gaze — on the moon as I tread — the drear wild, And — feel — that my
3. An ex - ile from home, splen-dor daz - zles in vain; Oh, — give — me my
p
mf
hum - ble, there's no — place like home; A — charm — from the skies seems to hal - low us
moth - er now thinks — of her child; As she looks — on that moon from our own — cot-tage
low - ly thatch'd cot - tage a - gain; The — birds — sing - ing gai - ly, that came — at my
mf
f
CHORUS
pp
there, Which, — seek — thro' the world, is ne'er met — with else-where. Home, home, —
door, Thro' the wood - bine whose fra - grance shall cheer — me no more. Home, home, —
call; Give me them, — and that peace of mind, dear - er than all. Home, home, —
f
pp
mf
sweet, sweet home, There's no — place like home, Oh, there's no — place like home.
mf

Sally in Our Alley

HENRY CAREY

Old English Air

Moderate, without dragging.
mp
1. Of all the girls that are so smart, There's none like pret- ty Sal - ly; She is the dar - ling of my heart,— And lives in our — al - ley; There is no la - dy in the land That's half so sweet as Sal - ly; She is the dar - ling of my heart, And — lives in our — al - ley.
2. Of all the days with- in the week, I dear - ly love but one day; And that's the day that comes be - twixt — The Sat - ur - day and Mon-day; Oh, then I'm dress'd all in my best, To walk a - broad with Sal - ly; She is the dar - ling of my heart, And — lives in our — al - ley.
3. My mas - ter and the neigh-bors all, Make game of me and Sal - ly, And but for her I'd rath - er be — A slave and row a gal - ley; But when my sev - en years are out, Oh, then I'll mar - ry Sal - ly; And then how hap - pi - ly we'll live, But — not in our — al - ley.

Then You'll Remember Me

MICHAEL BALFE
Arr. by G. M. Compagno

Moderately slow
1. When oth-er lips and oth - er — hearts Their tales of love will tell, In
2. When cold-ness of de - ceit — shall slight The beau-ty now they prize, And
lan - guage whose ex - cess — im - parts The pow'r they feel so well; There
deem it but a fad - ed — light Which beams with - in your eyes; When
may, per - haps in such — a — scene Some re-col - lec- tions be; Of
hol - low — hearts shall wear — a — mark 'Twill break your own to see; In
days that have as hap - py — been, And you'll re - mem - ber
such a mo - ment I — but — ask, That you'll re - mem - ber
rall.
me, — And you'll re - mem-ber, you'll re - mem - ber — me.
me, — That you'll re - mem-ber, you'll re - mem - ber — me.

Long, Long Ago

THOS. H. BAYLY

Andante
1. Tell me the tales that to me were so dear, Long, long a - go,
2. Do you re - mem -ber the path where we met, Long, long a - go,
3. Tho' by your kind -ness my fond hopes were raised, Long, long a - go,
Long, long a - go, Sing me the songs I de - light - ed to hear,
Long, long a - go, Ah, yes, you told me you ne'er would for - get,
Long, long a - go, You by more el - o - quent lips have been prais'd,
Long, long a - go, Long a - go. Now you are come, all my
Long, long a - go, Long a - go. Then, to all oth - ers my
Long, long a - go, Long a - go. But by long ab - sence your
grief is re - mov'd, Let me for - get that so long you have rov'd.
smile you pre - ferr'd, Love, when you spoke, gave a charm to each word,
truth has been tried, Still to your ac - cents I lis - ten with pride,
Let me be - lieve that you love as you lov'd, Long long a - go, Long a - go.
Still my heart treas-ures the prais -es I heard, Long long a - go, Long a - go.
Blest as I was when I sat by your side, Long long a - go, Long a - go.

Believe Me If All Those Endearing Young Charms

THOMAS MOORE

Arr. by G. M. Compagno

Moderately.
p
1. Be - lieve me, if all those en - dear - ing young charms Which I
2. It is not while beau - ty and youth are thine own, And thy
gaze on so fond - ly to - day, Were to change by to - mor - row, and
cheeks un - pro - fan'd by a tear, That the fer - vour and faith of a
fleet in my arms, Like fair - y gifts, fad - ing a - way, Thou would'st
soul can be known, To which time will but make thee more dear No, the
still be a - dored, as this mo - ment thou art, Let thy
heart that has tru - ly lov'd, nev - er for - gets. But as
love - li - ness fade as it will, And a - round the dear ru - in each
tru - ly loves on to the close, As the sun - flow - er turns on her
wish of my heart, Would en - twine it - self ver - dant -ly still.
god, when he sets, The same look which she turn'd when he rose.

The Rose of Tralee

C. MORDAUNT SPENCER
CHARLES W. GLOVER
Arr. by G. M Compagno
Moderately
p
1. The pale moon was ris - ing a - bove the green moun- tain, The sun was de - clin - ing be - neath the blue sea, When I stray'd with my love to the pure crys - tal foun - tain, that stands in the beau - ti - ful vale of Tra - lee: She was love - ly and fair as the rose of the summer, Yet 'twas not her beau - ty a - lone that won me, Oh, no! 'twas the truth in her eye ev - er dawn - ing, That made me love Ma - ry The Rose of Tra - lee.
2. The cool shades of eve - ning their man - tle were spread - ing, and Ma - ry all smil - ing was list - 'ning to me, The moon thro' the val - ley her pale rays was shed - ding, when I won the heart of the Rose of Tra - lee: Though love - ly and fair as the rose of the sum - mer, Yet 'twas not her beau - ty a - lone that won me, Oh, no! 'twas the truth in her eye ev - er dawn - ing, That made me love Ma - ry The Rose of Tra - lee.
mf
rit.

There's Music in the Air

GEORGE F. ROOT
Moderato con moto.
p
1. There's mu -sic in the air. When the in - fant morn is nigh And
2. There's mu -sic in the air. When the noon-tide's sul - try beam Re -
3. There's mu -sic in the air. When the twi-light's gen -tle sigh Is
faint its blush is seen On the bright and laugh - ing sky.
flects a gold - en light On the dis - tant moun - tain stream.
lost on eve - ning's breast As its pen - sive beau - ties die.
1. mf 2. pp
Man - y a harp's ec - stat - ic sound, With its thrill of joy pro - found,
When be - neath some grate - ful shade Sor - row's ach - ing head is laid
Then, O then the loved ones gone Wake the pure ce - les - tial song,
rit.
a tempo
1.2.
3.
While we list en - chant -ed there To the mu - sic in the air.
Sweet- ly to the Spir - it there Comes the mu - sic in the air.
An - gel voi - ces greet us there In the mu - sic in the air.

I Cannot Sing the Old Songs

Slowly, con espress.
Mrs. Charles Barnard (Claribel)
p
1. I can - not sing the old songs, I sang long years a - go, For
2. I can - not sing the old songs, Their charm is sad and deep; Their
3. I can - not sing the old songs, For vis - ions come a - gain Of
heart and voice would fail me, And fool - ish tears would flow; For
mel - o - dies would wa - ken Old sor - rows from their sleep, And
gold - en dreams de - part - ed And years of wea - ry pain, Per -
by - gone hours come o'er my heart, With each fa - mil - iar strain, I
tho' all un - for - got - ten still, And sad - ly sweet they be, I
haps when earth - ly fet - ters shall Have set my spir - it free, My
can - not sing the old songs, Or dream those dreams a - gain, I
can - not sing the old songs, They are too dear to me; I
voice may know the old songs, For all e - ter - ni - ty, My
cresc.
rall.
can - not sing the old songs, Or dream those dreams a - gain.
can - not sing the old songs, They are too dear to me.
voice may know the old songs, For all e - ter - ni - ty.

The Last Rose of Summer

THOMAS MOORE
FLOTOW
Andante
'Tis the last rose of summer, Left blooming alone
I'll not leave thee, thou lone one, To pine on the stem,
So soon may I follow, When friendships decay,
All her lovely companions Are faded and gone;
Since the lovely are sleeping, Go sleep thou with them;
And from love's shining circle The gems drop away;
No flower of her kindred, No rose bud is nigh,
Thus kindly I scatter Thy leaves o'er the bed,
When true hearts lie withered, And fond ones are flown,
To reflect back her blushes, Or give sigh for sigh.
Where thy mates of the garden Lie scentless and dead.
O who would inhabit This bleak world alone?

Flow Gently, Sweet Afton

Words by ROBERT BURNS

Music by J. E. SPILMAN

Andante con moto
p
1. Flow gen-tly, sweet Af-ton, a - mang thy green braes; Flow gen - tly, I'll sing thee a
2. How loft -y, sweet Af-ton, thy neigh-bor-ing hills, Far marked with the cours-es of
3. Thy crys-tal stream, Af-ton, how love-ly it glides, And winds by the cot where my
song in thy praise; My Ma-ry's a - sleep by thy mur-mur-ing stream, Flow gen-tly, sweet
clear wind-ing rills; There dai-ly I __ wan-der, as morn ris- es high, My flocks and my
Ma - ry re - sides! How wan-ton thy__ wa-ters her snow-y feet lave, As gath-'ring sweet
Af - ton, dis - turb not her dream. Thou stock-dove, whose ech - o re - sounds from the
Ma - ry's sweet cot in my eye. How pleas-ant thy banks and green val - leys be-
flow'r-ets, she stems thy clear wave! Flow gen - tly, sweet Af- ton, a - mang thy green
rit.
a tempo
hill, Ye__ wild whist-ling black-birds in yon thorn-y__ den, Thou green-crest-ed
low, Where wild in the wood-lands the prim- ros - es__ blow! There oft, as mild
braes, Flow gen- tly, sweet riv- er, the theme of__ my__ lays: My Ma - ry's a -
lap-wing, thy scream-ing for- bear, I charge you, dis -turb not my slum-ber-ing fair.
eve-ning creeps o - ver the lea, The sweet-scent-ed birk shades my Ma- ry and me.
sleep by thy mur-mur-ing stream, Flow gen - tly, sweet Af-ton, dis - turb not her dream.

Comin' thro' the Rye

Words bv ROBERT BURNS

Moderato
1. If a bod - y meet a bod - y, Com - in' thro' the rye,
2. If a bod - y meet a bod - y, Com - in' thro' the town,
3. 'Mong the twain there is a swain I dear-ly love my sel',

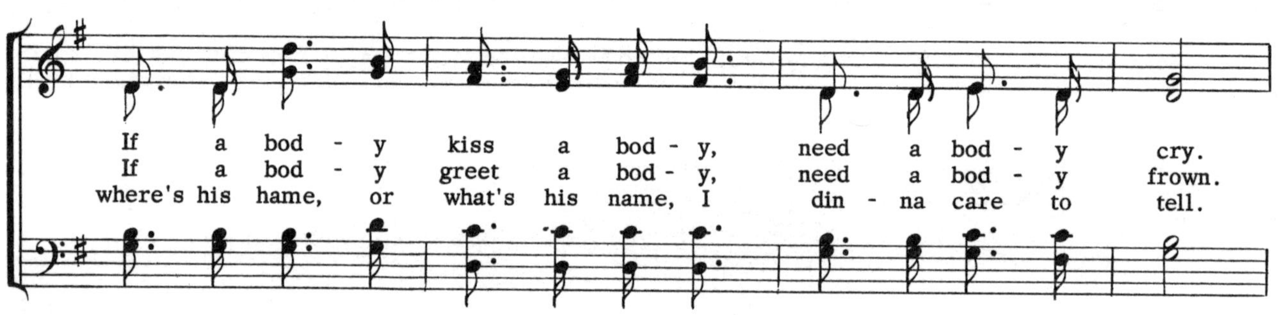
If a bod - y kiss a bod - y, need a bod - y cry.
If a bod - y greet a bod - y, need a bod - y frown.
where's his hame, or what's his name, I din - na care to tell.

3
Ev - 'ry las - sie has her lad - die, Nane they say have I Yet

all the lads they smile on me, When Com - in' thro' the rye.

John Anderson, My Jo

ROBERT BURNS

Air-Old Scottish

Andantino con moto.
mp
1. John An - der - son, my Jo, John, When we were
2. John An - der - son, my Jo, John, We've clamb the
first ac - quent, Your locks were like the ra - ven, John, Your
hills the - gith-er, And mo - ny a can - ty day, John, We've
bon - nie brow was brent; But now your brow is bald,
had wi' ane - a - nither; Now we maun tot - ter down,
John, Your locks are like the snow, But blessings
John, But hand in hand we'll go, And sleep the -
on your frost - y pow, John An - der - son, my Jo.
gith - er at the foot, John An - der - son, my Jo.

John Peel

Lively, with spirit.
Arr. by G. M. Compagno
1. Do ye ken John Peel with his coat so gay, Do ye ken John Peel at the break of the day, Do ye ken John Peel when he's far, far a - way, With his hounds and his horn in the morn - ing.
2. Do ye ken John Peel with his coat so gay, He lived at Trout-beck once on a day; But now he's gone far, far a - way, We shall ne'er hear his horn in the morn - ing.
rit.
a tempo
T'was the sound of his horn brought me from my bed, And the cry of his hounds which he oft - times led, Peel's "view hal - loo" would wak - en the dead, Or the
Tan- ta - ra Tan- ta - ra
Tan- ta - ra Tan- ta - ra
rit.
a tempo
1. fox from his lair, in the morn - ing.
2. rall.
fox from his lair, in the morn - ing.

Sailing, Sailing

GODFREY MARKS
Arr. by G. M. Compagno

With spirit.

Sail - ing, sail - ing, o - ver the bound- ing main;— For man- y a storm - y

wind shall blow, E're Jack comes home a - gain!— Sail - ing, sail - ing, o - ver the bound-ing

main; For man- y a storm - y wind shall blow, Ere Jack comes home a - gain.—

Alouette

Translation by
Don Titman

Arr. by G. M. Groene

Lively

Fine

A - lou - et - te, pret - ty A - lou - et - te, A - lou - et - te, I'll be on your trail.
A - lou et - te, gen tille A - lou - et - te, A - lou - et - te, Je te plu - me rai.

D. C. al Fine

Sure I'll clip your feathered head, Sure I'll clip your feathered head, *Et la tête* Ah.
Je te plu-me-rai la tête, Je te plu-me-rai la tête, Et le bec
Et les ailes
Et le dos
Et le queue
Et les pattes
Et le cou

Et la tête
Et le bec, etc.

In the measure before the "Ah" and the D.C. where the treble voices are echoed by the others, a word is added as each verse is sung, and the words of preceding verses are sung in reverse order. The duet in the last verse would be: Et le cou, et le cou, et les pattes, et les pattes, et le queue, et le queue, et le dos, et le dos, etc.

Little Brown Jug

Arr. by
Arthur Fields and Fred Hall

Gaily

1. My wife and I lived all a - lone In a lit - tle brown shack we called our own.
2. Had I a cow that gave such milk I would dress her in the fin - est silk.

She loved beer, and I loved rum; Tell you what it was, oh we had fun.
Feed her on the choic - est hay, And I'd milk her twen - ty times a day.

CHORUS

Ha, ha, ha, you and me, Lit - tle Brown Jug how I love thee,

Ha, ha, ha, you and me, Lit - tle Brown Jug how I love thee.

Drink to Me Only with Thine Eyes

BEN JONSON

Arr. by G. M. Compagno

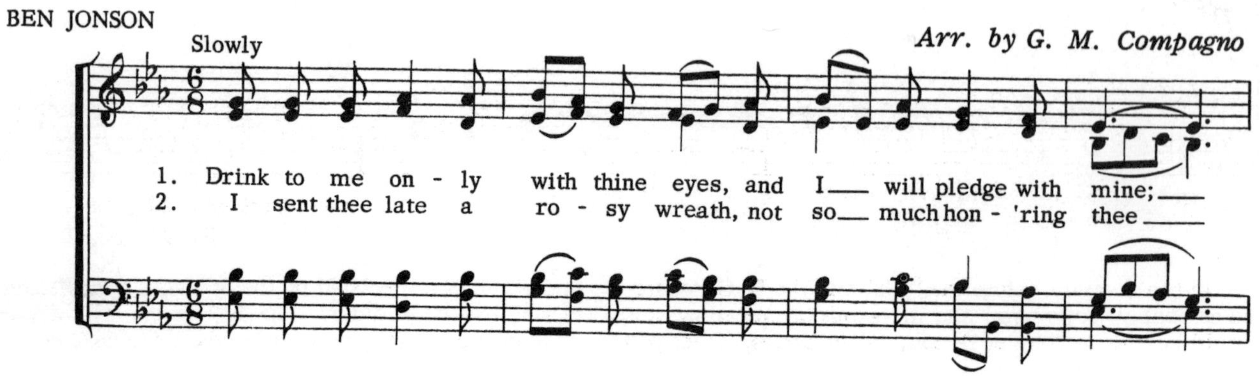
Slowly
1. Drink to me on - ly with thine eyes, and I ___ will pledge with mine; ___
2. I sent thee late a ro - sy wreath, not so ___ much hon - 'ring thee ___

Or leave a kiss with - in the cup, And I'll not ask for wine; The
As giv - ing it a hope that there It could not with - ered be But

thirst that from the soul doth rise Doth ask a drink di - vine;
thou there - on didst on - ly breathe, And sent'st it back to me,

But might I of Jove's nec - tar sup, I would-not change for thine.
Since when it grows and smells I swear, Not of it - self, but thee.

Blow the Man Down

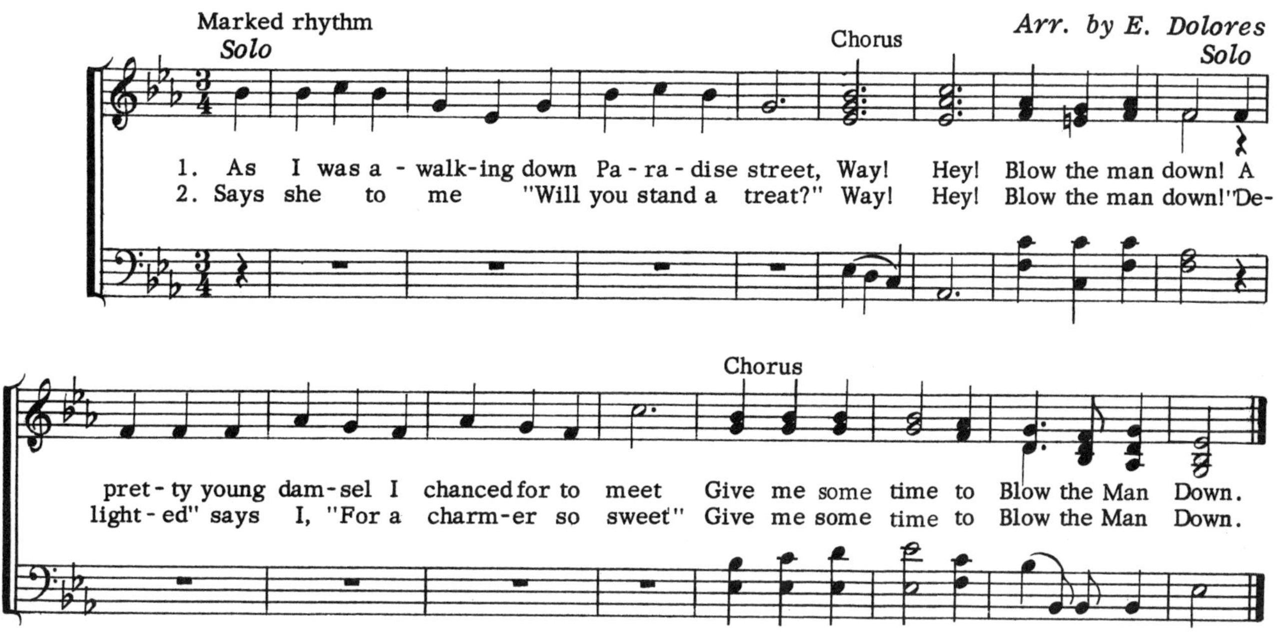
Marked rhythm
Solo
Chorus
Arr. by E. Dolores
Solo
1. As I was a - walk-ing down Pa - ra - dise street, Way! Hey! Blow the man down! A
2. Says she to me "Will you stand a treat?" Way! Hey! Blow the man down!"De-
Chorus
pret - ty young dam - sel I chanced for to meet Give me some time to Blow the Man Down.
light - ed" says I, "For a charm - er so sweet" Give me some time to Blow the Man Down.

A Capital Ship

Lyric by CHARLES E. CARRYL

Arr. by George Snowhill

Allegro
1. A cap - i - tal ship for an o - cean trip Was the
2. The bo - s'n's mate was ve - ry se - date, Yet
3. The cap - tain sat on the com - mo - dore's hat, And
Wal - lop - ing Win - dow Blind! No wind that blew dis -
fond of a - muse - ment, too; He played hop - scotch with the
dined in a roy - al way, Off toast - ed pigs and
- mayed her crew, Or trou-bled the Cap - tain's mind; The
star - board watch, While the cap - tain he tick-led the crew! And the
pick - les and figs And gun - ne - ry bread each day. And the
man at the wheel was made to feel Con - tempt for the wild - est
gun - ner we had was ap - par-ent - ly mad, For he sat on the aft - er
cook was Dutch, and be - haved as such For the di - et he gave the

blow - ow-ow, Tho' it oft - en ap-peared when the gale had cleared, That he'd been in his bunk be - low.
rai - ai -ail, And fired sa - lutes with the cap-tain's boots, In the teeth of the boom - ing gale!
crew- ew-ew, Was a num-ber of tons of hot cross buns Served up with su-gar and glue.
Then blow, ye winds, heigh - o! A - rov - ing I will go! I'll
stay no more on Eng- land's shore, So let the mu - sic play - ay - ay! I'm
off on the morn ing - train, I'll cross the rag - ing main! I'm
off to my love with a box - ing glove, Ten thou - sand miles a - way!

Oh, Promise Me

Lyric by CLEMENT SCOTT

REGINALD DE KOVEN
Arr. by Felix Guenther

Slowly
Oh promise me that some day you and I will
take our love to-geth-er to some sky. Where we can be a-lone, and faith re-
new. And find the hol-lows where those flow-ers grew. Those
first sweet vi-o-lets of ear-ly spring, Which come in whis-pers, thrill us
both, and sing Of love un-speak-a-ble that is to be; Oh

prom-ise me! Oh prom - ise me! Oh prom-ise me that you will take my
hand, The most un - wor - thy in this lone - ly land, And
let me sit be-side you, in your eyes, See - ing the vi - sion of our
par - a - dise, Hear - ing God's mes-sage while the or - gan rolls, Its
might - y mu - sic to our ver - y souls; No love — less per - fect than a
life with thee; Oh prom - ise me! Oh prom - ise me.

Parade of the Wooden Soldiers

Lyric by BALLARD MACDONALD

LEON JESSEL

Arr. by Ladislas Kun

March tempo
The toy - shop door is locked up tight and ev - 'ry - thing is
The dolls are in their best ar - rayed there's going to be a
p
toy - shop locked up all is still
dolls are ar - rayed to join a
Toy - shop locked up, all still
Dolls ar - rayed to join pa-
qui - et for the night, When sud - den - ly the clock strikes twelve the
won - der - ful pa - rade, Hark to the drum, oh here they come, cries
at night Now clock strikes twelve
pa - rade Look there they come,
now, clock strikes twelve
rade. Look, look they
fun's be - 1. gun. The 2. one. Now ev - 'ry bod - y
ev - 'ry - -
fun's be - gun.
ev - 'ry - one. Cheer them a-
fun's be - gun. ti - dy - um.
come, they come, ti - dy - um.
cheer them right a - long. There goes the drum ti - dy - um, ti - dy - um, tum - tum. And
long Drum beats tum - tum - tum.
Drum beats rum - tum - tum.

all the peo - ple lis - ten to the bells a - ring-ing Hark to the shout of the
There go the bells Hark, the
Hark, the
Cap - tain grand: Face a - bout! Right a - bout! As you were! Mark time!
Cap - tain shouts: Hark, the Cap - tain shouts:
(Melody)
Cap - tain shouts: Right, right, right a - bout For - ward,
For - ward! Let's go! All in a row!
For - ward! Let's go All in a row!
In
March! Right a - bout, Right a - bout!
Their un - i - forms bright-ly shine see them spark-ling in the sun The
Their un - i - forms bright-ly shine see them spark - le in the sun.
gay red un - i - forms each one is dressed up; they are spark - ling in the sun,
Their red un i forms shine bright in the
wood - en sol - diers all are out on a big pa - rade.
read - y for the big pa - rade.
sun all are out for the big pa - rade.

March - ing,
March - ing,
March - ing,
March - ing,
March - ing,
March - ing,
March-ing,
March-ing,
March-ing,
Step - ping for - ward,
Step-ping for - ward,
Step-ping for - ward,
March - ing
Chat-ter-ing bright-ly, flat-ter-ing light-ly, dressed in gowns so
March- ing.
Chat-ter-ing bright-ly, flat-ter-ing light-ly, dressed in gowns so
March-ing.
Hark
please make no
Step-ping for-ward. Chatt - 'ring gai - ly, flirt - ing
fine and smart.
Now they are meet - ing, see them all greet - ing Here and there bright
fine and smart.
Now they are meet - ing, see them all greet - ing Here and there bright
noise
See
their glanc - es
coy - ly, smart - ly dressed dolls wel - come
glanc - es dart
Pret - ti - ly shy they wit - ti - ly try to pierce a wood - en
glanc - es dart
Pret - ti - ly shy they wit - ti - ly try to pierce a wood- en
dart
Try
to pierce a
sol - diers Each dart aims to pierce a
sol - dier's heart, as they stiff - ly come a - march ing Bent up-on real fun, ti - tum - tum! The
sol - dier's heart, as they stiff - ly come marching tum - - tum - tum - tum!
sol - dier's heart, as they stiff - ly go march-ing rum - - tum - tum - tum!

toy - shop door is still locked tight and wood - en sol - diers fro - lic through the night And
see the sol - dier's pass - ing by and there's an im - pish hap - py lit - tle twink' a
Toy - shop locked tight, they fro - lic all night
Now see sol - diers there is a twin - kle
Shop is still locked tight, they think
See, oh! see, there is a twink'
all the while they think of naught but fun just fun. Now
flash - ing from each
They think of naught but high fun.
in each
of naught but fun just fun, ti - dy - um.
sol - dier's eye. Here they are Hur - - rah!
boy's eye Here they are Hur - - rah!
boy's eye Here they are Hur - - rah!
Glow Worm
Lyric by
LILLA CAYLEY ROBINSON
PAUL LINCKE
Arr. by Ladislas Kun
Moderato
When the night falls si - lent - ly, the night falls
Lit - tle glow - worm, tell me pray, oh glow-worm
When the night falls si - lent - ly, the night falls
Lit - tle glow - worm tell me pray, oh glow-worm
When soft falls the night
Glow - - worm tell me pray,

si - lent - ly on for - ests dream - ing, Young folks wan - der
tell me pray, how did you kin - dle, Lamps that by the
night falls on for - ests dream - ing, Young folks wan - der
tell me how did you kin - dle, Lamps that now you
falls on for - ests dream - ing, Young
oh tell me, how you kin - dle, Lamps
forth to see they wan - der forth to see the bright stars gleam - ing,
break of day, that by the break of day, must fade and dwin - dle,
forth just to see the bright stars, the bright stars gleam - ing,
kin - dle must fade and dwin - dle, must fade and dwin - dle,
folks wan - der forth, they go to see stars gleam - ing,
that bright - ly shine, but soon de - cline and dwin - dle,
And lest they should lose their way lest they should lose their way the glow-worms
"Ah this se - cret, by your leave, this se - cret, by your leave, is worth while
And lest they should lose their way lit - tle glow - worms, the glow-worms
"Ah, this lit - tle se cret is worth while learn - ing, is worth while
And lest they should lose their for - est way,
And so by your leave. this se cret learn,
night - ly Light their ti - ny lan - terns gay, their ti - ny
learn - ing, When the young folks come at eve, the young folks
night - ly, Light their ti - ny lan - terns, their ti - ny
learn - ing, When young folks come at eve, young folks come
lit - tle glow - worms night - ly, Light their lan - terns so gay,
it is worth while learn - ing, When young folks come at eve,
mf

lan-terns gay and twin-kle bright - ly. Here and there, and
come at eve, their hearts are yearn - ing. Glow-ing eyes and
p
p
lan - terns and twin - kle bright - ly. Here and
at eve, their hearts are yearn - ing. Eyes be -
p
lan - terns that shine bright - ly.
hearts ev - 'ry - one yearn - ing.
ev - 'ry - where from mos - sy dell and hol - low,
lips be tray, how sweet youth's glad - ness tast - ed!
there from mos - sy hol - low,
tray how glad - ness tast - ed!
From mos - sy
Bright glow - ing
They call on us to fol - low, to fol - low!
We steal the fire, lest it should be wast - ed!"
pp
pp
They will call on us to fol - low!
Fire we steal, lest it be wast - ed!
Float - ing, glid - ing through the air, they call on us to fol - low!
Till we steal the fire a - way, for fear, lest it be wast - ed!
mp
pp
dell they call, they call on us to fol - low!
eyes and lips be - tray how glad-ness tast - ed!
M M M M
M M M M
M M M M

Shine, lit - tle glow - worm, glim - mer, Shine, lit - tle glow - worm,
Shine, lit - tle glow - worm, glim - mer, Shine lit - tle glow - worm,
Lit - tle glow - worm, glim - mer, Lit - tle glow - worm,
glim - mer, Lead us, lest too far we wan - der, Love's sweet voice is
glim - mer, Lead us, lead
glim - mer, Lead us, lest too far we wan - der, Love's sweet voice is
glim - mer, Lead us, Lead
call - ing yon-der! Shine lit - tle glow-worm, glim - mer, Shine lit-tle glow-worm
us,
Shine lit - tle glow - worm glim - mer, Shine lit - tle glow - worm
call - ing yon - der!
us, Lit - tle glow - worm, glim - mer, Lit - tle glow - worm,
glim - mer, Light the path, be - low a - bove, and lead us on to
glim - mer, Light the path, be - low a - bove, and lead us on to
glim - mer, Light, light be - low, a - bove, and lead us on to
Love! Ah Ah
Love! Ah Ah
Love! Shine lit-tle glow-worm, glim - mer, Shine, lit - tle glow-worm
Love! Glow - worm glim - mer, Glow - worm

Lead, lest too far we wan - der
(Melody)
Love's voice is
Love's sweet voice is call - ing
glim - mer,
Lead us, lit - tle star,
Lest we wan - der
(Melody)
glim - mer,
Lead us, lest too far we
call - ing yon - der!
(Melody)
Lit - tle glow - worm, oh shine and glim - mer,
yon - der!
(Melody)
Shine, lit - tle glow - worm, glim - mer,
far
Ah
wan - der!
Love's sweet voice is
Love's sweet voice is call - ing yon - der,
Light the path be -
(Melody)
Shine, lit - tle glow - worm, glim - mer,
Light the path be -
Ah
call - ing yon - der,
Light, light be -
low a - bove, and lead us on to Love!
low a - bove, and lead us on to Love!
low a - bove, and lead us on to Love!

Still as the Night

English Words by
ALBERTO SILVIO

CARL BOHM
Arr. by G. M. Compagno

Moderato, with expression.
mp
Still as the night, Vast as the sea,
Still wie die Nacht. Tief wie das Meer,
p
rit.
a tempo
mf
So is my love for thee.
Soll dei-ne Lie - be sein.
Humming
(for thee.)
(lie-be sein.)
mf
cresc.
ff
Still as the night, (the night) And vast as the sea, So is my
Still wie die Nacht, (die Nacht) Und tief wie das Meer, Soll dei - ne
(as the sea,)
(wie das Meer,)
rit.
a tempo
love for thee, my love for thee. So is my love for thee.
Lie-be, dei - ne Lie - be sein, Soll dei-ne Lie - be sein.
(my love)
(lie - be)
rit.
Coda ad lib. Vocal or Piano.
mp
Humming
pp

Juanita

Andante
1. Soft o'er the foun - tain, Lin - g'ring falls the south-ern moon;
2. When in thy dream-ing, Moons like these shall shine a - gain,
Far o'er the moun-tain, Breaks the day too soon!
And day - light beam - ing Prove thy dreams are vain,
In thy dark eye's splen-dor, Where the warm light loves to dwell,
Wilt thou not, re - lent - ing, For thine ab - sent lov- er sigh,
Wea- ry looks, yet ten - der, Speak their fond fare - well!
In thy heart con - sent - ing, To a pray'r gone by?
3
Ni - ta! Jua - ni - ta! Ask thy soul if we should part!
Ni - ta! Jua - ni - ta! Let me lin - ger by thy side!
Ni - ta! Jua - ni - ta! Lean thou on my heart!
Ni - ta! Jua - ni - ta! Be my own fair bride!

Cielito Lindo

English adaption by
CAROL RAVEN
C. FERNANDEZ
Arr. by G. M. Compagno
Brightly
1. Wild bird that leaves your nest in the eaves, Re - mem-ber what I am
2. If you should fall in love as we all do, Guard well your heart's af -
1. Pa - ja - ro que a - ban - do - na su pri - mer ni - do, su pri - mer
2. Siem-pre que te e - na - mo - res imi - ra pri - me - ro mi - ra pri -
say-ing, Don't ev - er roam too far from home, Love may fly a - way
fec-tion, Tears of - ten start when lov - ers part, Leav-ing on - ly fond
ni - do Si loen-cuen - tra o cu - pa - do cie - li - to lin - do muy
me - ro. Don - de po - nes los o - jos cie - li - to lin - do no
while you're stray-ing.
re - col - lec - tion.
me - re - di - so.
llo - res lue - go.
CHORUS
Beau - ti - ful Heav'n Lies
Ay ay ay ay can -
all a - round you, But Heav'n is best in a co - sy nest. When a
ta y no llo - res, Por que can - tan - do se a - le - gran cie - li - to
beau - ti - ful love has found you. love has found you.
lin - do los co - ra - zo - nes. co - ra - zo - nes.
1.
2.

La Golondrina

(THE SWALLOW)

English Lyrics by MARJORIE HARPER

N. SERRADELL
Arr. by G. M. Compagno

Moderately fast
mf
A Chief-tain brave, when leav-ing old Gra - na - da, Felt heart and
A - ben Ha - met al par-tir de Gra - na - da, Su co - ra -
soul with grief and an-guish spent. And as the light of that fair land so
zon tras-pa-sa do sin - tio, Ya-lla en la Ve - ga al per-der-la de
with expression
bright, Van-ished from his sight, He voiced his sad la - ment. Fair land I
vis - ta con de-bil voz, Su la-men-to ex-pre-so. Man-sion de a-
love, I am leav-ing thy bos-om for ev - er! I know that
mo res ce-les-tial pa-ra - i - so. Na-ci en tu
nev - er shall I gaze on thee more. No more to dwell, 'neath the joy of thy
se - no, Y mil di-chas go-ce, Voy a par- tir, A le-ja-nas te-
spell! Now I say Fare-well Dear land that I a - dore. Fair land I dore.
gio nes De don-de nun - ca, Ja-mas vo-ve - re Man-sion de a re.
1.
2.

A Media Luz

(WHEN LIGHTS ARE SOFT AND LOW)

English version by
BERT CHILD
Spanish lyric by A. LENZI
E. DONATO
Arr. by George Snowhill
Moderato
p
Oh come to me in the ev' - ning When
Co - rrien - tes tres cua - tro o - cho Se -
the sun hides in the west
gun - do piso as - cen - sor.
I am ev - er of you
No hay por-teros ni ve
dream- ing
ci - nos
When at night I go to rest.
A - den - tro cock-tail ya - mor
Oh
Pi -
come to my arms my loved one,
si - to que pu - so Ma - ple;
Clasp me to your arms so
Pia - no, es - te - ray ve la
dear,
dor.
The stars will pro - tect you, sweet one
Un te - le - fón que con - tes - te

Please tell that you will be mine dear,___ We will dance un - til the
U - na vic - tro - la que llo - ra___ Vie-jos tan - gos de mi
dawn, till the sun comes in the morn, And the shades of night will be gone.
flor y un ga - to de por - ce - la - na pa' que no maulle el a - mor.
CHORUS
When lights are soft and low my lone- ly heart's a - glow with love for you my
Y todo a me-dia luz que es un bru - jo el a - mor A me-dia luz los
dear I see a vis- ion so clear. I feel a pas - sion rare As it be - gins to
be - sos a me - dia luz los dos Y to - do a me-dia luz, Cre-pus-cu- lo in- te -
flare My love's be - yond com - pare When lights are soft and low.
rior, Que sua - ve ter - cio - pe - lo La me - dia luz de a - mor.
D.S.
Fine

Ay, Ay, Ay

English Lyrics by
MARJORIE HARPER

OSMAN PEREZ FREIRE
Arr. by G. M. Compagno

Moderately
Look out of thy win - dow, please, Ay, Ay, Ay, Sweet
A só - ma te a la ven - ta - na ay, ay, ay, pa-
Dove of my soul I call to thee. Then let me with - in thy heart, Ay, Ay, Ay, Sweet
lo-ma del al-ma mi - a. A só-ma te a la ven - ta - na ay, ay, ay, pa-
love of my soul pray come to me! The star - lit sky has be - come gray; Be-
lo ma del al - ma mi - a que ya la au-ro-ro tem-pra - na. Nos
hold: The dawn of the new day! Look out of thy win - dow dear - est
vin ne a nun - ciar el di - a. Que ya la au - ro - ra tem -
one, Ay, Ay, Ay, A bove us the sun is on its way.
pra na ay, ay, ay, Nos vie-ne an - un - ciar el di - a.

Allá en el Rancho Grande

English lyric by BARTLEY COSTELLO
Spanish lyric by SILVANO R. RAMOS
Music by SILVANO R. RAMOS
Arr. by Freeman High
Moderately fast
I love to roam out yon - der, Out where the Buf - f'lo wan - der, Free
A - llá en el ran-cho gran-de, A - lla don-de vi - vi - a, Ha -
as the Eag-le fly-ing, I'm rop-ing and a - ty-ing, I'm rop-ing and a - ty-ing,
bia n na ran-che ri - ta Que a-le-gre me de- ci - a, Que a-le-gre me de - ci - a.
Give me my ranch and my cat - tle, Far from the
Give me my bri - dle and sad - dle, And my old
Te voy ha - cer tus cal - zo - nes, Co - mo los
great cit - y's rat - tle; Give me a big
Pin - to I'll strad - dle; I'll get the cow -
u - sa el ran - che - ro; Te los co - mien -
herd to bat - tle, For I just love herd - ing cat - tle.
boys a - rid - ing, Out where the rust - lers are hid - ing.
zo de la - na, Te los a - ca - bo de cue-ro.

La Violetera
(WHO'LL BUY MY VIOLETS?)

English lyric by FRANCIA LUBAN
Spanish lyric by EDUARDO MONTESINOS

Music by JOSE PADILLA
Arr. by J. Rosamond Johnson

Moderato
Won't some - bod - y buy my vi - o - lets?
Lle - ve - lo us - ted se - ño - ri - to,
(my vi - o -
(no - ri -
Lit - tle flow - ers so di - vine.
No va - le más que un re al.
Wear these po - sies to all
Com - pre - me us - té es te ra -
lets?)
to)
(flow - ers so di - vine.)
le mas que un re - la
plac - es, And you'll sure - ly bright - en fa - ces, For they'll cheer you just like
mi - to, Com - pre - me us - té es - te ra - mi - to, Pa lu - cir lo en el ho -
wine.
jal.
Won't some - bod - y buy my vi - o - lets?
Lle - ve - lo us - té se - ño - ri - to,
(They'll cheer you like wine)
(lu - cir - lo en ho - jal)
(my vi - o -
(no - ri -
Take them while they're fresh with dew,
No va - le mas que un re - al,
Give your loved one flow - ers
Com - pre - me us - té es - te ra
lets?)
While they're fresh with dew)

3
dai - ly, And you'll see her wear so gai - ly, Vi- o - lets I of - fer
mi - to, Com-pre - me us-té es-te ra - mi - to, Pa lu - cir-lo en el ho-
1.
2.
you. (I of - fer you) Won't some-bod - y buy my you. (I of - fer you)
jal. (lo en el ho - jal.) Lle - ve-lo us -té se - ño - jal. (lo en el ho - jal.)

White Wings

By BANKS WINTER

Arr. by George Snowhill

Moderato

"White Wings," they nev - er grow wea - ry, They car - ry me cheer-i - ly

o - ver the sea; Night comes, I long for my dear - ie, I'll

spread out my "White Wings" and sail home to thee! Sail home!

fz

The Peanut Vendor

Lyric by MARIAN SUNSHINE
Novelty lyric by L. WOLFE GILBERT
Music by
MOISES SIMONS
Arr. by Oscar Catsiff
Intro. With rhythm
f
La, la, la, la, la, la, la, la, la, la, la. La, la, la, la, la, la,
La, la, la, la, La,
la, la, la, la, la, In Cu - ba each mer - ry maid Makes up to
la, la, la, la, la, la, la, la,
Pea - nuts Pea - nuts
this ser - e-nade Pea - nuts They're nice and hot Pea - nuts
la, la la Fresh toast-ed La They're toast-ed
If you have-n't got ba - na - nas, don't be blue
I sell a lot Mm
Pea - nuts in a lit - tle bag are call - ing you.
Mm Mm
Mm
Don't waste them, No tum - my ache

You'll taste them when you a - wake. For at the ver - y break of day.
La, la, la, la, La, la, la, la,
at dawn - ing that whis - tle blows
The pea-nut ven - dor's on his way
la, la, la, la, at dawn-ing that whis - tle blows
Thru ev-ry ci ty, town and coun - try land. You'll hear him sing his plain -
la, la, la, la, la, la,
- tive lit - tle strain, And as he pass - es you, he will say
la, la, la, la, la, la,
Mm Mm Mm Pea - nuts roast-ed to-day
Big jum-ble, Big dou - ble ones, Come buy those now.

Fresh-ly roast-ed to-day, If you're look-ing for a
Come try those now,
mor - al to this song.
Fif - ty mil - lion lit - tle mon-keys can't be wrong
la, la, la, la,
I go
I go
Man - yan - na
La, I'll look for this street a-gain La.
I go
I'll sell them You'll eat a-gain
we'll meet a-gain
la, la, la, la,
la
That pea - nut man's gone.
Your pea - nut man

Ciribiribin

English Lyrics by
ALBERTO SILVIA

A. PESTALOZZA
Arr. by G. M. Compagno

Waltz tempo
Ci-ri -bi -ri - bin, your ten - der glance turns dark - est night to bright -est
Ci-ri-bi-ri - bin, che bel fac - cin, che sguar-do dol - ce a - sas-
day, Ci -ri - bi - ri - bin, will our ro - mance still live when years have
sin, Ci-ri-bi -ri - bin, che bel na - sin, che bel den - tin, che
passed a - way. Ci -ri -bi - ri - bin you're so di - vine, Tell
bel boc - chin! Ci-ri-bi -ri - bin che bel fac - cin, che
me you're mine be - fore we part, Ci -ri -bi - ri - bin,
sguar - do dol - ce as - sas - sin Ci-ri-bi -ri - bin,
Ci -ri -bi -ri - bin, Ci- ri -bi -ri - bin, Give me your heart.
Ci-ri-bi-ri - bin, Ci-ri-bi -ri -bin, che bel fac - cin.

O Sole Mio

Italian Lyric by
G. CAPURRO
English Lyric by
OLGA PAUL

Music by
E. di CAPUA

Arr. by George Snowhill

Andantino
1. Oh day of beau - ty when the sun is shin - ing
2. When sun-light fades and night be - gins her brood - ing
1. Che bel - la co - sa 'na - iur - na - ta'e so - le,
2. Quan - no fa not - te'o so - le se ne scen - ne,
The air is calm a - gain, the storm is end - ed;
My lone - ly heart is sad, and full of an - guish,
N'a - ria se - re - na dop po 'na tem - pes - ta!
Mme ve - ne qua - se 'na ma - lin - co - ni - a,
The scent of flow - ers with the breeze is blend - ed, Oh day of
I stand be - neath your win dow while I lan - guish, When sun-light
Pe' ll'a - ria fres - ca pa - re gia 'na fes - ta Che bel - la
Sott' 'a fe - nes - ta to - ia res - tar - ri - a, Quan - no fa
3
beau - ty when the sun is shin - ing.
fades and night be - gins her brood - ing.
co - sa 'na iur - na - ta'e so - le!
not - te'o so - le se ne scen - ne.
But there is sun - light
Ma n'a - tu so - le

that's bright - er far, Than an - y sun - beam or an - y
cchiù bel - lo, ohi - ne', 'O so - le mi - o sta 'nfron-te a

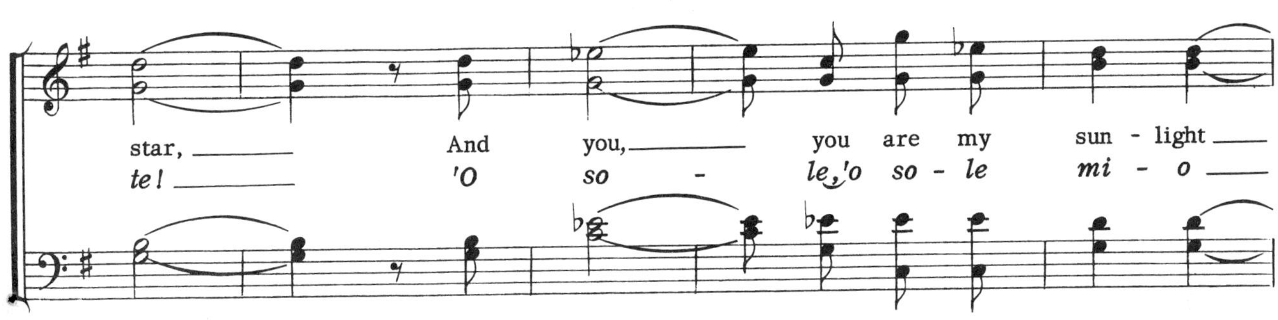
star, And you, you are my sun - light
te! 'O so - le, 'o so - le mi - o

that's bright - er far, Than sun or star!
sta 'nfron-te a te, sta 'nfron - te a te!

The Jolly Miller

Arr. by George Snowhill

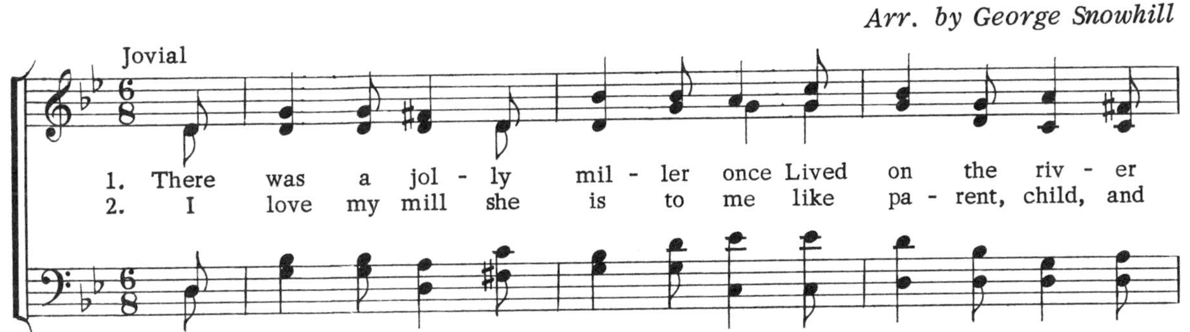
Jovial
1. There was a jol - ly mil - ler once Lived on the riv - er
2. I love my mill she is to me like pa - rent, child, and

Dee, He work'd and sang from morn till night, No lark more blithe than
wife. I would not change my sta - tion For a - ny o - ther in

he. And this the bur - den of his song For - e - ver used to
life. Then push the bowl, the bowl, my boys, And pass it round to

be, I care for no - bo - dy, no, not I, If no - bo - dy cares for me.
me. The long - er we sit here and drink, The mer - ri - er we shall be.

I'll Take You Home Again, Kathleen

T.B. WESTENDORF
Arr. by George Snowhill
Andantino
Oh! I will take you back, Kath - leen, To
where your heart will feel no pain, And when the fields are fresh and

a - gain.
green, I'll — take you to your home a - gain, a - gain.

Whispering Hope

ALICE HAWTHORNE

Arr. by George Snowhill

Slow Waltz tempo

Whis - per - ing whis - per - ing hope — Oh, how

wel - come thy voice — how wel - come, mak - ing my

heart in it's sor - row re - joice, — re-

1. joice. —

2. re - joice, — re - joice.

Santa Lucia

Andante
mp
1. Now 'neath the sil - ver moon o - cean is glow - ing, o'er the calm
2. When o'er Thy wa - ters light winds are play - ing, thy spell can
bil - low, soft winds are blow - ing, Here balm - y zeph - yrs blow,
soothe us, all care al - lay - ing. To thee, sweet Na - po - li,
Pure joys in - vite — us, and as we gent - ly row, All things de - light us.
What charms are giv - en where smiles cre - a - tion, Toil blest by hea - ven.
Hark, How the sail - or's cry joy - ous - ly ech - oes nigh. San - ta — Lu -
Home of fair po - es - y, realm of pure har - mon - y, San - ta — Lu -
ci - a! San - ta Lu - ci - a! Hark, How the sail - or's cry
ci - a! San - ta Lu - ci - a! Home of fair po - es - y,
joy - ous - ly ech - oes nigh, San - ta - Lu - ci - a! San - ta Lu - ci - a!
realm of pure har - mon - y, San - ta - Lu - ci - a! San - ta Lu - ci - a!

Come Back to Sorrento

English Words by
DON TITMAN
E. DE CURTIS
Arr. by G. M. Compagno
Moderato, with animation
See how beau-ti - ful the o - cean, Like your deep blue eyes a - danc - ing,
Guar-da il ma-re co-me bel - lo! spi-ra tan-to sen-ti men-to
rit.
Stirs my heart in fond de - vo - tion, Sets me dream-ing, dear, of you.
Co me il tuo soa - ve ac - cen - to che me des-to fa so - gnar.
mf
Blos-soms wave a beck-'ning fin - ger, Or - ange boughs shed lov - ers' per-fume,
Sen - ti co - me lie - ve sa - le dai giar - di - nio - dor d'a - ran - ci
Bid you trav - 'ler, here to lin - ger, All so gent - ly plead with you.
Un pro - fu - mo non v'ha e gua - le per chi pal - pi - ta d'a - mor!
Still your an - swer "I am leav - ing!" Laugh-ing proud - ly, un - be - liev - ing
E tu di - ci Io par-to ad - di - o! T'al lon - ta - ni dal mio co - re
Slowly with expression
rit.
That you left a lov - er griev - ing, And you broke a heart so true.
ques - ta ter - ra dell 'a - mo - re hai la for - za di la - sciar?

Funiculi, Funicula

English Words By
EDW. OXENFORD
Music by LUIGI DENZA
Arr. by G. M. Compagno
Animated.
Solo
mf
Some think the world is made for fun and frol - ic And so do
Sta se - ra Ni - na mia, io son mon - ta - to Te lo di-
Solo and Chorus
Solo
I! And so do I Some think
ro Te lo di - ro Co - la
it well to be all mel - an - chol - ic To pine and sigh
do - ve di - spet - tu in cor in - gra - to Piu far non puo
Solo and Chorus
Solo
To pine and sigh But I I love to spend my time in
Piu far non puo Co - la con cen te il fo - co ma se
Solo and Chorus
sing - ing Some joy - ous song Some joy - ous song
fu - ggi Ti la - scia star Ti la - scia star

Solo
To set the air with mu - sic brave - ly ring - ing
E non ti cor - re ap - pres - so, e non ti strug - gi
Solo and Chorus
is far from wrong! Is far from wrong.
A ri - guar - dar A ri - guar - dar
CHORUS
p
Lis - ten! Lis - ten! Ech - oes sound a - far! Lis - ten! Lis - ten!
Les - ti, Les - ti, via, mon - tiam su - la Les - ti, Les - ti,
Ech - oes sound a - far! Fu - ni - cu - li, fu - ni - cu - la, fu - ni - cu - li, fu - ni - cu -
via, mon - tiam su - la, Fu - ni - cu - li, fu - ni - cu - la, fu - ni - cu - li, fu - ni - cu -
1. 2.
la, Ech - oes sound a - far, Fu - ni - cu - li, fu - ni - cu - la. Oh! la!
la, via mon - tiam su - la, Fu - ni - cu - li, fu - ni - cu - la. Ah! la

Oh, Marie

English Words by
F. A. GROENE
E. DI CAPUA
Slowly, with expression.
Arr. by G. M. Compagno
Oh, Ma - rie Oh, Ma - rie In my
Ah, Ma - ri! Ah, Ma - ri! Quan - ta
slum-ber I'm dream-ing of thee! Come to my heart, And tell
suon-no che per- do per te; Fam m'ad - dur - mi, Ab-brac-
me tru - ly you do love me. Oh, Ma - rie Oh, Ma -
cia- to nu po - co cu te! Ah, Ma - ri! Ah,Ma-
rie I am wait - ing for you, can't you see
ri! Quan-to suon- no che per- do pe te!
We'll nev - er part! Ah Ma - rie! Ah Ma - rie!
Fam m'ad - dur - mi, Ah Ma - ri! Ah Ma - ri!

Drigo's Serenade

English Words by
SIGMUND SPAETH
Italian Words by
CESARE STURANI

R. DRIGO
Arr. by M. G. Groene

Moderately
Come where the moon-path is bright, come where the
Vien! la scia la bu-ia la-gu-na Vien, al-lo splen
sea turns to light, Ah, come, to the lure of the night, and
dor del-la lu-na, Vien, al ri-chia-mo d'a-mor, E at-
speed an-oth-er dawn-ing day! Come do not tar-ry too
ten-di del nuo-vo di l'al-bor. Vien, non tar-dar, mio te-
long, Come, to the sound of my song, Ah, come hear love's
sor, Vien, al mio gri-do d'a-mor Ah! vien, il mio de-
heart beat-ing strong with pow'r to draw you far a-way.
si-o ti vuo-le Por-tar con se lon-tan, lon-tan.
3

Tit Willow

W. S. GILBERT

SIR ARTHUR SULLIVAN
Arr. by George Snowhill

Moderato
1. On a tree by a riv - er a lit - tle tom - tit Sang
2. He slapped at his chest as he sat on the bough, Sing - ing
3. Now I feel just as sure as I'm sure that my name Isn't
"wil-low, tit - wi - low, tit - wi - low!" And I said to him," Dick - y bird,
"wil-low, tit - wi - low, tit - wi - low!" And a cold per - spi - ra - tion be -
wil-low, tit - wi - low, tit - wi - low, That 'twas blight-ed af - fec - tion that
why do you sit Sing - ing wil - low, tit - wi - low, tit - wi - low? Is it
span-gled his brow, Oh, wil - low, tit - wi - low, tit - wi - low. He
make him ex-claim "Oh, wil - low, tit - wi - low, tit - wi - low!" And if
weak - ness of in - tel - lect, bird - ie," I cried, "Or a rath - er tough worm in your
sobbed as he sighed and a gur - gle he gave, Then he threw him-self in - to the
you re - main cal - lous and ob - du - rate, I shall per - ish as he did and
lit - tle in - side?" With a shake of his poor lit - tle
bil - low - y wave, And an ech - o a - rose from the
you will know why, Though I prob - ab - ly shall not ex -

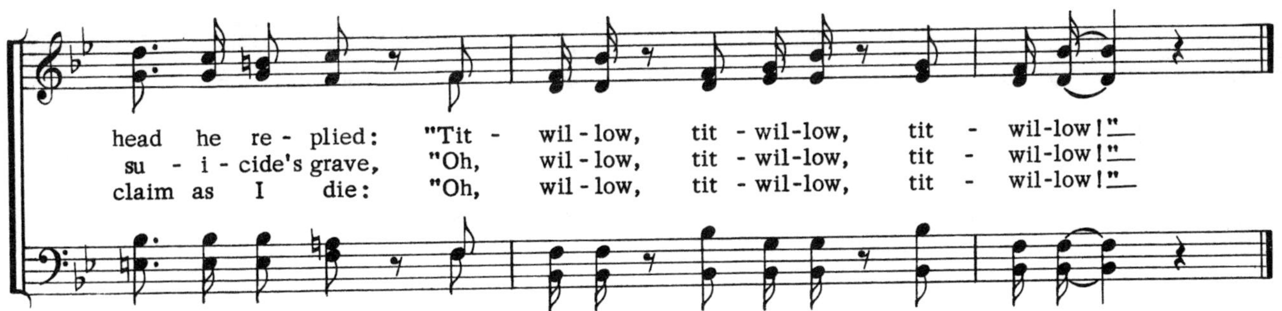
head he re - plied: "Tit - wil - low, tit - wil-low, tit - wil-low!"
su - i - cide's grave, "Oh, wil - low, tit - wil-low, tit - wil-low!"
claim as I die: "Oh, wil - low, tit - wil-low, tit - wil-low!"

The Flowers that Bloom in the Spring

W. S. GILBERT

SIR ARTHUR SULLIVAN
Arr. by George Snowhill

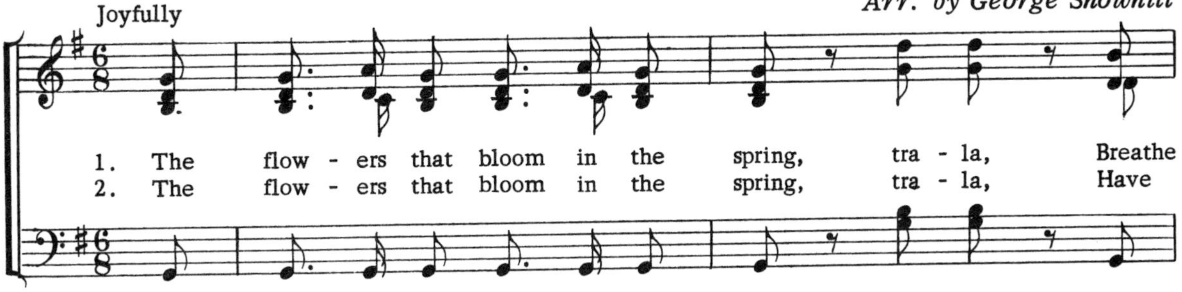

Joyfully

1. The flow - ers that bloom in the spring, tra - la, Breathe
2. The flow - ers that bloom in the spring, tra - la, Have

prom - ise of mer - ry sun - shine, — As we mer - ri - ly dance and we
noth - ing to do with the case. — I've — got to take un - der my

sing, tra - la, We wel - come the hope that they bring, tra - la, Of a
wing, tra - la, A most un - at - tract - ive old thing, tra - la, With a

sum - mer of rose - es and wine, Of a sum - mer of ros - es and wine, And
car - i - ca - ture of a face, With a car - i - ca-ture of a face, And
that's what we mean where we say that a thing Is wel-come as flow - ers that
that's what I mean when I say or I sing, "Oh, both - er the flow - ers that
bloom in the spring. Tra la la la, la Tra la la la la, The
bloom in the spring." Oh,
flow - ers that bloom in the spring. Tra la la la la, Tra
both - er the flow - ers of spring.
la la la la, Tra la la la la la.

A Wand'ring Minstrel

SIR ARTHUR SULLIVAN
W.S. GILBERT *Arr. by George Snowhill*

Moderato
A wan-d'ring mins-trel I, A thing of shreds and patch-es, of
bal - lads, songs and snatch-es, And dream - y lul - la - by! My
ca - ta - logue is long, through ev' - ry pas - sion rang - ing, And
to your hum - ours chang-ing I tune my sup - ple song!
I tune my sup - ple song!

We Sail the Ocean Blue

W. S. GILBERT

SIR ARTHUR SULLIVAN
Arr. by Oscar Catsiff

Allegretto
We — sail the o - cean blue, and our sau - cy ship's a
beau - ty; We're — so - ber men and true and at - ten - tive to our
du - ty; When the balls whis - tle free o'er the bright — blue sea, we
stand — to our guns all day, — When at an - chor we ride on the
Ports - mouth tide, we've plen - ty of time for play a - hoy! a-
Mm —

Mm
hoy! the balls whis-tle free. A - hoy! a - hoy! The balls whis-tle
free, we stand to our guns, to our guns all day We
sail the o - cean blue, And our sau - cy ship's a beau - ty, We're
so - ber men and true and at - ten - tive to our du - ty, our
sau - cy ship's a beau - ty, We're at - ten - tive to our du - ty, We're
so - ber men and true, we sail the o - cean blue.

Three Blind Mice

Allegro
Three blind mice, Three blind mice,
1st Voice
2nd Voice
3rd Voice
4th Voice
See how they run, See how they run, They all run af - ter the
Three blind mice, Three blind mice, See how they
Three blind
farm-er's wife, She cut off their tails with a carv- ing knife; Did ev - er you see such a
run, See how they run, They all ran af - ter the
mice, Three blind mice, See how they
Three blind
thing in your life, as cut off their tails with a carv - ing knife,
farm - er's wife, She Did ev -er you see such a
run, See how they run, They all ran af -ter the
mice, Three blind mice, See how they
ev - er you see such a
thing in your life, as Three blind mice.
farm - er's wife, she cut off their tails with a carv - ing knife, Did
run, See how they run, they all ran af - ter the

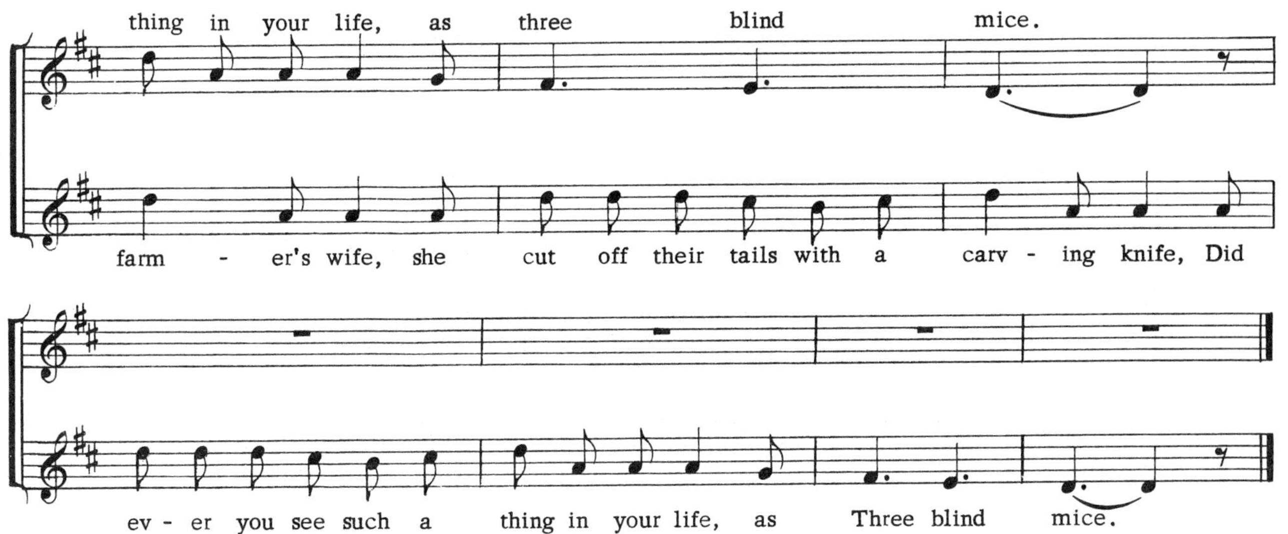
thing in your life, as three blind mice.
farm - er's wife, she cut off their tails with a carv - ing knife, Did
ev - er you see such a thing in your life, as Three blind mice.

Who Threw the Overalls in Mistress Murphy's Chowder?

By GEORGE L. GIEFER

Arr. by George Snowhill

Moderato

"Who threw the o - ver - alls in Mis - tress Mur - phy's chow - der?"

No - bod - y spoke so he shout - ed all the loud - er: "It's an

I - rish trick that's true, I can lick the Mick that threw the

o - ver - alls in Mis - tress Mur - phy's chow - der."

Reuben and Rachel

Arr. by George Snowhill

Allegretto
1. Reu-ben, Reu-ben, I've been think-ing what a grand world this would be.
2. Reu-ben, Reu-ben, I've been think-ing what a gay life girls would lead.
3. Reu-ben, Reu-ben, Stop your teas-ing if you've an-y love for me.
If the men were all trans-port-ed Far be-yond the north-ern sea.
If they had no men a-bout them, None to tease them, None to heed.
I was on-ly just a-fool-ing, As I thought of course you'd see.
Oh my good-ness gra-cious, Ra-chel, What a queer world this would be
Ra-chel, Ra-chel, I've been think-ing, Men would have a mer-ry time,
Ra-chel, if you'll not trans-port us, I will take you for my wife,
If the men were all trans-port-ed far be-yond the north-ern sea.
If at once they were trans-port-ed far be-yond the salt-y brine.
And I'll split with you my mon-ey ev'-ry pay-day of my life.

Row, Row, Row Your Boat

Arr. by George Snowhill

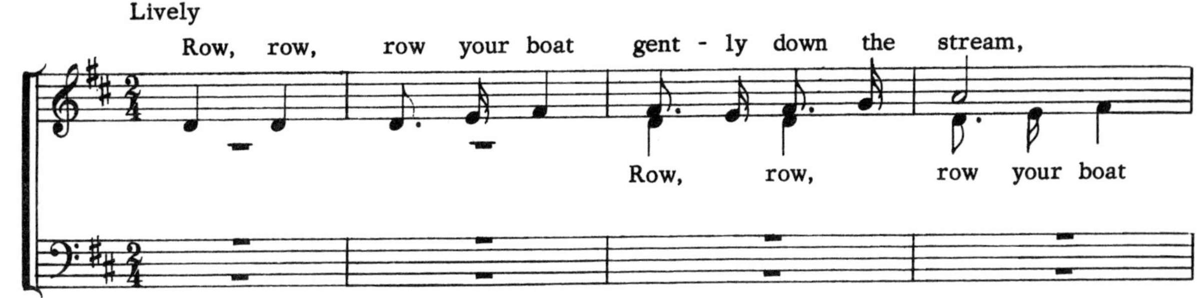
Lively
Row, row, row your boat gent - ly down the stream,
Row, row, row your boat

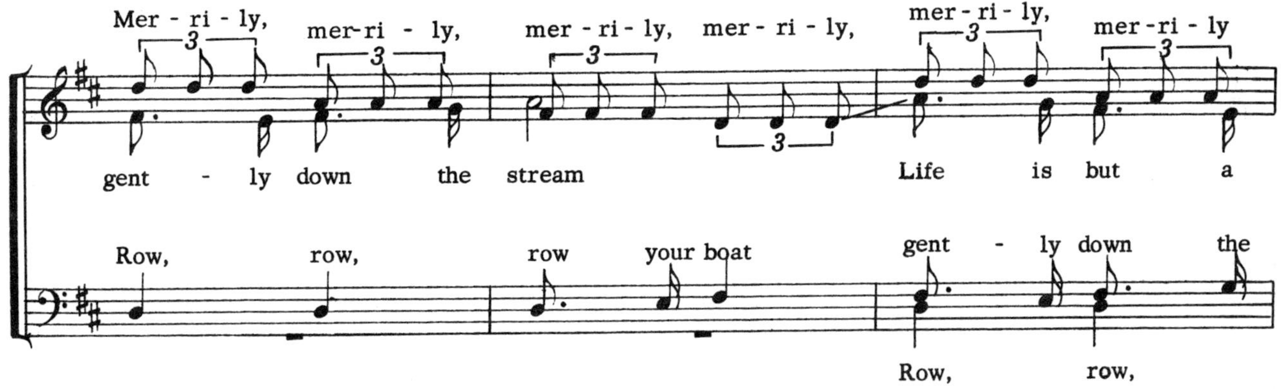
Mer - ri - ly, mer-ri - ly, mer - ri - ly, mer - ri - ly, mer - ri - ly, mer - ri - ly
gent - ly down the stream Life is but a
Row, row, row your boat gent - ly down the
Row, row,

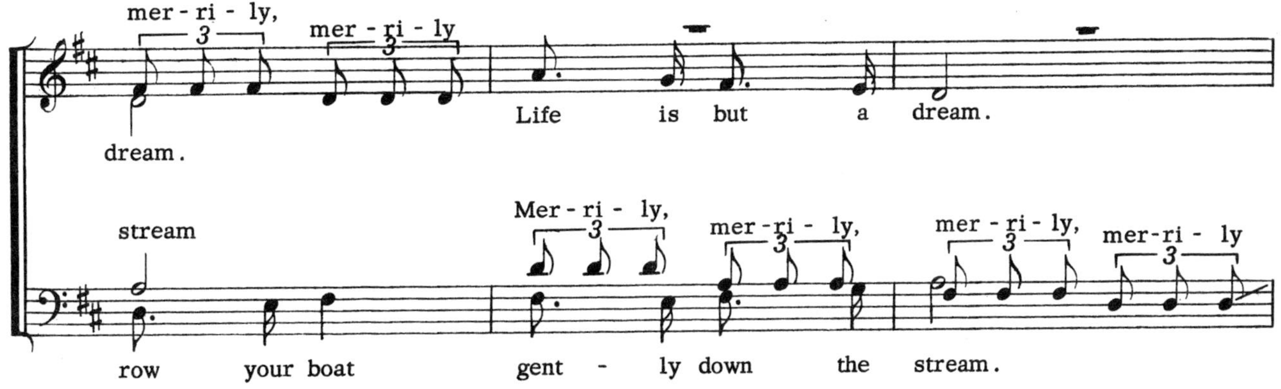
mer - ri - ly, mer - ri - ly
dream. Life is but a dream.
stream Mer - ri - ly, mer - ri - ly, mer - ri - ly, mer - ri - ly
row your boat gent - ly down the stream.

Mer - ri - ly, mer - ri - ly, mer - ri - ly, mer - ri - ly
Life is but a dream. Life is but a dream.

Oh, How Lovely Is the Evening

Moderato
Arr. by George Snowhill
Soprano
Alto
Oh, how love - ly is the eve - ning,
is the eve - ning, when the bells are
Oh, how love - ly
sweet - ly ring - - ing, sweet - ly ring - ing;
is the eve - ning, is the eve - ning,
Ding Dong Ding Dong, Ding Dong,
when the bells are sweet- ly ring - ing, sweet- ly ring - ing
Oh, how love - ly is the eve - ning, is the eve - ning,
Ding Dong, Ding Dong, Ding Dong,
when the bells are sweet - ly ring - ing, sweet - ly ring - ing,
Oh, how love - ly is the eve - ning, is the eve - ning,
Ding Dong, Ding Dong, Ding Dong.
when the bells are sweet - ly ring - ing, sweet - ly ring - ing!
Ding Dong.
Ding Dong, Ding Dong, Ding Dong.

Frère Jacques

French Round
Moderato
1st Group
Are you sleep - ing? Are you sleep - ing? Fri - ar John, Fri - ar John,
Frè - re Jac-ques, Frè - re Jac-ques, Dor-mez vous? Dor-mez vous?
2nd Group
Are you sleep - ing? Are you sleep - ing?
Frè-re Jac-ques, Frè - re Jac-ques,
Set the chimes a-ring-ing, Set the chimes a-ring ing Ding, Ding, Dong! Ding, Ding, Dong!
Son-nez les ma-ti-nes, Son-nez les ma-ti-nes, Din, Din, Don! Din, Din, Don!
Fri - ar John, Fri - ar John, Set the chimes a-ring-ing, Set the chimes a-ring-ing,
Dor - mez vous? Dor - mez vous? Son-nez les ma-ti-nes, Son-nez les ma-ti-nes
3rd Group
Are you sleep-ing? Are you sleep-ing? Fri - ar John, Fri - ar John,
Frè - re Jac-ques, Frè - re, Jac ques, Dor - mez vous? Dor - mez vous?
4th Group
Are you sleep - ing? Are you sleep-ing?
Frè - re Jac-ques, Frè - re Jac-ques,
Are you sleep-ing? Are you sleep-ing? Fri - ar John, Fri - ar John,
Frè - re Jac-ques, Frè - re Jac-ques, Dor - mez vous? Dor - mez vous?
Ding, Ding, Dong! Ding, Ding, Dong! Are you sleep-ing? Are you sleep -ing?
Din, Din, Don! Din, Din, Don! Frè - re Jac-ques, Frè - re Jac-ques,
Set the chimes a-ring-ing, Set the chimes a-ring-ing, Ding, Ding, Dong! Ding, Ding, Dong!
Son-nez les ma-ti-nes, Son-nez les ma-ti-nes, Din, Din, Don! Din, Din, Don!
Fri - ar John, Fri - ar John, Set the chimes a-ring-ing, Set the chimes a ring-ing,
Dor - mez vous? Dor - mez vous? Son-nez les ma-ti-nes, Son-nez les ma-ti-nes,

Lullaby

JOHANNES BRAHMS

Arr. by G. M. Groene

Tenderly
p
1. Lul - la - by and good night! With ros - es be- dight, creep in - to thy bed, There pil - low thy head. If God will, thou shalt wake when the morn - ing doth break, If God will, thou shalt wake, when the morn - ing doth break.
2. Lul - la - by and good night; Those blue eyes close tight; bright an - gels are near, So sleep with - out fear. They will guard thee from harm with fair dream-land's charm, They will guard thee from harm with fair dream-land's charm.
1. Gu - ten A bend, gut' Nacht, mit Ro - sen be- dacht, mit Näg - lein be - steckt, schlumpf' un - ter die Deck; Mor - gen früh, wenn Gott will, wirst du wie - der ge- weckt Mor - gen früh wenn Gott will, wirst du wie - der ge - weckt.
2. Gu - ten A bend, gut' Nacht, von Eng - lein be- wacht, die zei - gen im Traum dir Christ - kind - leins Baum: Schlaf' nun se - lig und süss, schau 'im Traum's Pa - ra - dies. Schlaf' nun se - lig und süss, schau'im Traum's Pa - ra - dies.
p

Cradle Song

Music by
FRANZ SCHUBERT

English Words by
F.R.R.

Arr. by Oscar Catsiff

Moderato
p
1. Sweet - ly slum - ber 'neath the or - chard shad - ows,
2. Sweet - ly slum - ber o'er thine eye - lids ten - der,
3. Sweet - ly slum - ber while I bear thee home - ward;
p
near thee murm - 'ring soft the brook - let flows;
or - chard blos - soms waft their fra - grant snows;
heav'n grows dark - er, cold an east wind blows;
winds of spring - time gen - tly lull thee
may they wake not may they bring thee
in these arms sleep soft - ly, dar - ling
moth - er's dar - ling, moth - er's op - 'ning rose.
an - gel vi - sions, dew - y deep re - pose.
moth - er's love, no change no cold - ness knows.

Sweet and Low

ALFRED TENNYSON

JOSEPH BARNBY

Larghetto
pp
1. Sweet and low, sweet and low, Wind of the west - ern
2. Sleep and rest, sleep and rest, Fa - ther will come to thee
pp
sea; Low, low, breathe and blow, Wind of the west - ern
soon; Rest, rest on moth - er's breast, Fa - ther will come to thee
sf
p
mf
sea; O - ver the roll - ing wa - ters go, Come from the dy - ing
soon; Fa - ther will come to his babe in the nest, Sil - ver sails all
pp
f
moon and blow, Blow him a - gain to me,
out of the west, Un - der the sil - ver moon:
p
rall. e dim.
While my lit - tle one, while my pret - ty one sleeps.
Sleep, my lit - tle one, sleep, my pret - ty one, sleep.

Go to Sleep, Lena Darling

J.K. EMMET

Arr. by George Snowhill

Moderato

Close your eyes, Le - na, my dar - ling, While I sing your lul - la -

by; Fear thou no dan-ger, Le-na; Move not, dear Le - na, my dar - ling, For your bro-ther watch-es

nigh you, Le - na dear. An-gels guide thee, Le-na dear, my dar - ling,— Noth-ing e - vil

can come near; Bright-est flow-ers bloom for thee, Dar - ling— sis-ter, dear to— me.

CHORUS

Go to sleep, go to sleep my ba - by, my ba - by, my ba - by, Go to sleep, my ba - by,—

ba - by, on, bye! Go to —— sleep, Le - na, sleep.

All Through the Night

H. BOULTON

Old Welsh Song
Arr. by G. M. Compagno

Slowly
p
1. Sleep, my love, and peace at - tend thee All through the night;
2. While the moon her watch is keep - ing All through the night;
Guard - ian an - gels, God will lend thee, All through the night.
While the wea - ry world is sleep - ing All through the night.
mf
Soft the drow - sy hours are creep - ing, Hill and vale in slum - ber steep - ing,
O'er thy spir - it gent - ly steal - ing, Vi - sions of de - light re - veal - ing,
softly
Love a - lone his watch is keep - ing All through the night.
Breathes a - pure and ho - ly feel - ing All through the night.

All God's Chillun

Arr. by Florence White

Jubilantly
1. I got shoes, you got shoes, All God's chil-lun got shoes;
2. I got wings, you got wings, All God's chil-lun got wings;
3. I got a harp, you got a harp, All God's chil-lun got a harp;
When I get to heav-en, gon-na put on my shoes; I'm gon-na walk all o-ver God's heav-en,
When I get to heav-en, gon-na put on my wings, I'm gon-na fly all o-ver God's heav-en,
When I get to heav-en, gon-na play on my harp, I'm gon-na play all o-ver God's heav-en,
Heav-en, Heav-en;
Ev-'ry-bod-y talk-in' 'bout heav-en ain't go-in' there,
Heav-en, Heav-en, Gon-na walk all o-ver God's heav-en.

Git on Board

Arr. by J. Rosamond Johnson

Lively.
mp
Ooh - ooh, ooh - ooh.
Git on board lit-tle
mf
On board lit- tle
chil - dren, git on board lit - tle chil -dren, Git on board lit - tle
chil - dren, git on board, on board lit- tle chil -dren, on board lit- tle
1. Git on
2. The
chil - dren, There's room for man-y - a more. more.
Gos- pel train am com - in' I hear it close at hand, I
(Humming)
hear the car - wheels mov - in' and rumb-lin' thru the land. The

fare is cheap and all can go, The rich and poor are dere. No
sec - ond class a - board dis train, no dif - f'rence in de fare. Git on
board lit - tle chil - dren, Git on board lit - tle
on board lit - tle chil - dren, Git on board, on board lit - tle
chil - dren, Git on board lit - tle chil - dren
chil - dren, on board lit - tle chil - dren Dere's
poco a poco rall.
room for man- y - a more. Oo - oo, oo - oo.
f
mp
pp

Swing Low, Sweet Chariot

Arr. by George Snowhill

Slowly
Swing low Sweet char - i - ot Com-ing for to car-ry me home, Oh
Swing low sweet char - i - ot Com-ing for to car-ry me home. Oh home. Oh
look ov - er Jor - dan an what did I see Com-ing for to car-ry me home, A
you get - a there be fo' I do Com-ing for to car-ry me home, Tell
band of an - gels com-ing af-ter me Com-ing for to car-ry me home. If
all of my friends I'm com - ing too Com-ing for to car-ry me home home.
Swing low sweet char - i - ot Com-ing for to car-ry me home, Oh
Swing low sweet char - i - ot Com-ing for to car-ry me home.
1.
2.

Joshua Fit de Battle of Jericho

Arr. by J. Rosamond Johnson

Lively, with marked rhythm.
Josh-ua fit de bat-tle of Jer-i-cho, Jer-i-cho, Jer-i-cho.
Josh-ua fit de bat-tle of Jer-i-cho An'de walls come tumb-lin' down. (Dat morn-in') down.
1.
2.
You may talk a-bout yo' King o' Gi-de-on You may talk a-bout yo' man o' Saul. Dere's none like good old Josh-ua, At de bat-tle of Jer-i-cho.
Humming
At de bat-tle of Jer-i-cho.
(Yes)
Josh-ua fit de bat-tle of Jer-i-cho, Jer-i-cho, Jer-i-cho.
molto rall.
Josh-ua fit de bat-tle of Jer-i-cho, An' de walls come tumb-lin' down.

Wade in the Water

Traditional Melody
Arr. by
EDGAR ROGIE CLARK

Andante Maestoso.
Wade in the water, wade in the water children,
Wade in the water, God's goin' to trouble the water.
rit.
Look over yonder what do I see,
Hum Hum
rit.
God's goin' to trouble the water.
A band of Angels comin' after me.
Hum Hum
rit.
God's goin' to trouble the water.
in the water, in the water, wade my children, wade in the water children,
wade in the water, wade in the water children
in the water, in the water, wade my children, wade in the water children,

wade, dim. wade.
wade, wade. God's goin' to trou- ble,
wade, in the wa - ter.
wade, dim. wade.
rit. dim.
the wa - ter See that host all dressed in white God's goin' to trou-ble the
rit.
wa - ter. The lead - er looks like a Is - rael - ite. God's goin' to trou - ble the
cresc. child - ren, wa - ter child- ren wade dim.
wade wa - ter child- ren wade
wa-ter. O Wade the wa - ter wade in the wa - ter child-ren, in the
wade the wa - ter child- ren wade dim.
Wade Wade, rit.
Wade Wade,
wa - ter in the wa - ter, in the wa - ter, God's goin' to trou - ble the
Wade Wade, rit.
rit. Oh, wade! Lunga
wa - ter. Child- ren, wade the, wa-ter, child- ren

Go Down, Moses

Negro Spiritual
Arr. by
J. Rosamond Johnson

Majestic
(well sustained)
Go down Mo - ses, Way down in E - gypt land
Tell ole Pha - a - a - roah, To let my peo - ple go.
When Is - rael was in E - gypt's land,
Spoke the Lord, bold Mo - ses said:
Let my peo-ple go. Op -
If
Humming
pressed so hard they could not stand,
not I'll smite your first born dead,
Let my peo-ple go. Thus go.
1.
2.

Oh Dem Golden Slippers

By JAMES A. BLAND
Arr. by George Snowhill

Moderato
Oh, dem gold - en slip - pers! Oh, dem
gold - en slip - pers! Gold - en slip - pers I'se gwine to wear, Be -
kase dey look so neat; Oh, dem gold - en slip - pers!
Oh, dem gold - en slip - pers! Gold - en slip - pers I'se
gwine to wear, To walk de gold - en street.

Nobody Knows de Trouble I See

Slowly (with feeling)
Arr. by George Snowhill
No - bod - y knows de troub-le I see, No - bod - y knows but Je - sus;
No - bod - y knows de troub-le I see, Glo - ry hal - le - lu - jah! Oh,
No - bod - y knows de troub-le I see, No - bod - y knows but Je - sus;
No - bod - y knows de troub-le I see, Glo - ry Hal - le - lu - jah! Some-
times I'm up Some - times I'm down, Oh, yes, Lord; Some -

times I'm al - most to de ground, Oh, yes, Lord. Al -
tho' you see me goin' 'long so, Oh, yes, Lord: I
have my troub -les here be - low, Oh, yes, Lord. Oh!
No - bod - y knows de troub-le I see, No - bod - y knows but Je - sus;
No - bod - y knows de troub - le I see, Glo - ry hal - le - lu - jah!

Oh, a Rock-a-My Soul

Arr. by J. Rosamond Johnson

With spirit
mf
Oh, a Rock-a my soul In the bo-som of A-bra-ham, a
mf
Rock-a my soul In the bo-som of A-bra-ham, a
Rock-a my soul In the bo-som of A-bra-ham,
Solo
When I went down in the val-ley to pray,
oh, Rock-a my soul.
mp
pp Hum
My soul got hap-py and I stayed all day,
oh, Rock-a my soul.
Hum

When I was a mourn - er just like you,
oh, Rock- a my soul. Hum
I mourned and mourned 'till I come through,
oh, Rock- a my soul. Hum
oh, Rock - a my soul. Oh, a Rock - a my soul In the
bo - som of A - bra- ham, a Rock - a my soul In the
bo - som of A - bra - ham, a Rock - a my soul In the
rall.
bo - som of A - bra - ham, oh, Rock - a my soul.

Deep River

Arr. by George Snowhill

Andante quasi Lento
Deep ——— Ri - ver, My home is o - ver
Jor - dan, —— Deep ——— Ri - ver, Lord, I want to cross o - ver in - to
camp - ground, Lord, I want to cross o - ver in - to camp ground, —— Lord, I
want to cross o - ver in - to camp ground. Oh, don't you want to go to that
Gos - pel - feast, That Prom - ised Land, where all is peace? Oh,

don't you want to go to that Gos - pel - feast, That Prom - ised Land, where
all is peace? Deep Ri - ver, My home is o - ver
Jor - dan, Deep Ri - ver, Lord, I
want to cross o - ver in - to camp ground, Lord, I want to cross o - ver in - to
camp ground, Lord, I want to cross o - ver in - to camp ground.

Roll, Jordan, Roll

Arr. by George Snowhill

Allegro moderato
1.
2.
Roll Jor - dan roll, Roll Jor - dan roll, I
want 'a go to heav'n when I die To hear old Jor - dan roll. O, breth - er - en, roll. Oh,
broth - ers you ought - er been there,
sis - ters you ought - er been there,
Yes my Lord.
Set - tin' up in the King - dom, for to hear old Jor - dan roll. Oh, roll.
Roll Jor - dan roll. Roll Jor - dan roll, I
want 'a go to heav 'n when I die, To hear old Jor - dan roll.

Little David, Play on Your Harp

Negro Spiritual
Arr. by J. Rosamond Johnson

Lively
Lit -tle Dav -id play on your harp, Hal- le - lu, hal - le - lu, Lit-tle Dav-id
1.
2.
play on your harp, Hal- le - lu Hal-le-lu, hal-le - lu, Lit-tle Dav-id lu. Lit-tle
1. Dav-id was a Shep-herd boy
2. Josh-ua was the Son of Nun
He killed Go - li - a' an' shout-ed for joy.
Humming
He nev-er would quit 'till his work was done.
Lit- tle Dav - id play on your harp, Hal - le - lu, hal - le - lu, Lit-tle Dav - id
Repeat for 2nd verse D.S.
Last time.
Fine.
play on your harp, Hal - le - lu. Ol' lu jah!

Steal Away

Arr. by George Snowhill

Slowly
mp
Steal — a-way, steal — a-way, Steal — a-way to Je-sus!
3
Steal — a-way, steal a-way home, I ain't got long to stay here.
p
Steal — a-way, steal — a-way, Steal — a-way to Je-sus.
Fine
Steal — a-way, steal a-way home, I ain't got long to stay here.

f
p
My Lord, He calls me, He calls me by the thun-der, The trump-et sounds_ with-

in - a my soul I ain't got long to stay here.

f
p
Green trees a' bend-ing, po' sin - ner stand a trem-bling, The trump-et sounds_ with-

D. C. al Fine
in - a my soul I ain't got long to stay here.

Hark! the Herald Angels Sing

CHARLES WESLEY

FELIX MENDELSOHN - BARTHOLDY

Moderately fast
1. Hark! the her - ald an - gels sing, "Glo - ry to the new - born King!
2. Christ, by high - est heav'n a - dored, Christ, the ev - er - last - ing Lord:
3. Hail, the heav'n-born Prince of Peace! Hail, the Sun of Right-eous - ness!
Peace on earth, and mer - cy mild; God and sin - ners rec - on - ciled!"
Long de - sired, be - hold Him come, Find - ing here His hum - ble home.
Light and life to all He brings, Ris'n with heal - ing in His wings.
Joy - ful, all ye na tions, rise; Join the tri - umph of the skies;
Veiled in flesh the God - head see, Hail th' in - car - nate De - i - ty!
Let us then with an - gels sing, "Glo - ry to the new - born King!
(2nd time)
With th' an - gel - ic hosts pro - claim, "Christ is born in Beth - le - hem!"
Pleased as man with men to dwell, Je - sus our Im - man - u - el.
Peace on earth and mer - cy mild; God and sin - ners rec - on - ciled!"

Joy to the World

ISAAC WATTS

GEORGE F. HANDEL

With spirit
1. Joy to the world! the Lord is come; Let earth re - ceive her King; Let ev - 'ry heart pre - pare Him room, And heav'n and na - ture sing, And heav'n and na - ture sing, And heav'n, and heav'n and na - ture sing.
2. Joy to the earth! the Sav - ior reigns; Let men their songs em - ploy; While fields and floods, rocks, hills and plains Re - peat the sound - ing joy, Re - peat the sound - ing joy, Re - peat, re - peat the sound -ing joy.
3. He rules the world with truth and grace, And makes the na - tions prove The glo - ries of His right - eous - ness, And won - ders of His love, And won - ders of His love, And won-ders, and won - ders of His love.
1. And heav'n and na - ture sing,
And heav'n and na - ture sing,

O Little Town of Bethlehem

Words by PHILLIPS BROOKS

Music by LEWIS REDNER

Moderato

1. O lit - tle town of Beth - le - hem, How still we see thee lie!
2. O morn-ing stars to - geth - er Pro - claim the ho - ly birth,

A - bove thy deep and dream - less sleep The si - lent stars go by.
And prais - es sing to God the King, And peace to men on earth.

Yet in thy dark streets shin - eth The ev - er - last - ing light;
For Christ is born of Ma - ry And ga - ther'd all a - bove,

The hopes and fears of all the years Are met in thee to - night.
While mor - tals sleep, the an - gles keep Their watch of won - d'ring love.

It Came Upon the Midnight Clear

Words by EDWIN H. SEARS

Music by R. S. WILLIS

Moderato
1. It came up - on the mid - night clear, That glo - rious song of old,
2. Still through the clo - ven skies they come With peace-ful wings un - furled;

From An - gels bend - ing near the earth, To touch their harps of gold:—
And still their heav'n - ly mu - sic floats O'er all the wea - ry world;—

"Peace on the earth, good - will to men, From heav-en's all gra - cious King."—
A - bove its sad and low - ly plains They bend on hov - 'ring wing,—

The world in sol - emn still - ness lay To hear the An - gels sing.—
And ev - er o'er its Ba - bel sounds The bless - ed An - gels sing.—

We Wish You a Merry Christmas

Arr. by Florence White

Gaily.
We wish you a mer- ry Christ-mas, We wish you a mer-ry
Christ- mas, We wish you a mer-ry Christ- mas, and a hap - py New Year.

O Come, All Ye Faithful

(ADESTE FIDELES)

JOHN READING

Majestically
p
O come, all Ye Faith - ful, Joy - ful and tri - um - phant, O
A - des - te, Fi - de - les, Lae - ti tri - um - phan - tes, Ve-
come ye, O come ye to Beth - le - hem. Come and be - hold Him,
ni - te, ve - ni - te, in Beth - le - hem. Na - tum vi - de - te,
8
pp
Born the King of An - gels: O come, let us a - dore Him, O
Re - gem an - ge - lo - rum. Ve - ni - te, a - do - re - mus, Ve -
cresc.
mf
come let us a - dore Him, O come let us a - dore Him, Christ the Lord.
ni - te, a - do - re - mus, Ve - ni - te a - do - re - mus, Do - mi - num.

The First Noël

Traditional

Espressivo
1. The— first— No - ël the— an - gel did say Was to cer- tain poor
2. They— look - ed— up and— saw— a star Shin-ing in— the
3. This— star— drew— nigh to— the— north - west, O'er— Beth - le
4. Then— en - ter'd— in there— Wise - men three, Full— rev - 'rent
shep-herds in fields as they lay; In— fields— where— they lay—
East— be - yond— them far, And— to— the— earth it—
hem— it took— its rest, And— there— it— did both—
ly— up - on— their knee, And— of - fer'd— there in—
keep- ing their sheep On a cold win- ter's night— that was— so deep.
gave— great light, And— so it con - tin - ued both day— and night.
stop— and stay Right— o - ver the place— where Je - sus lay.
His— pres - ence, Their— gold— and myrrh— and frank - in - cense.
CHORUS
No - ël,— No - ël, No - ël, No - ël,— Born is the King— of Is - ra - el.

Away in a Manger

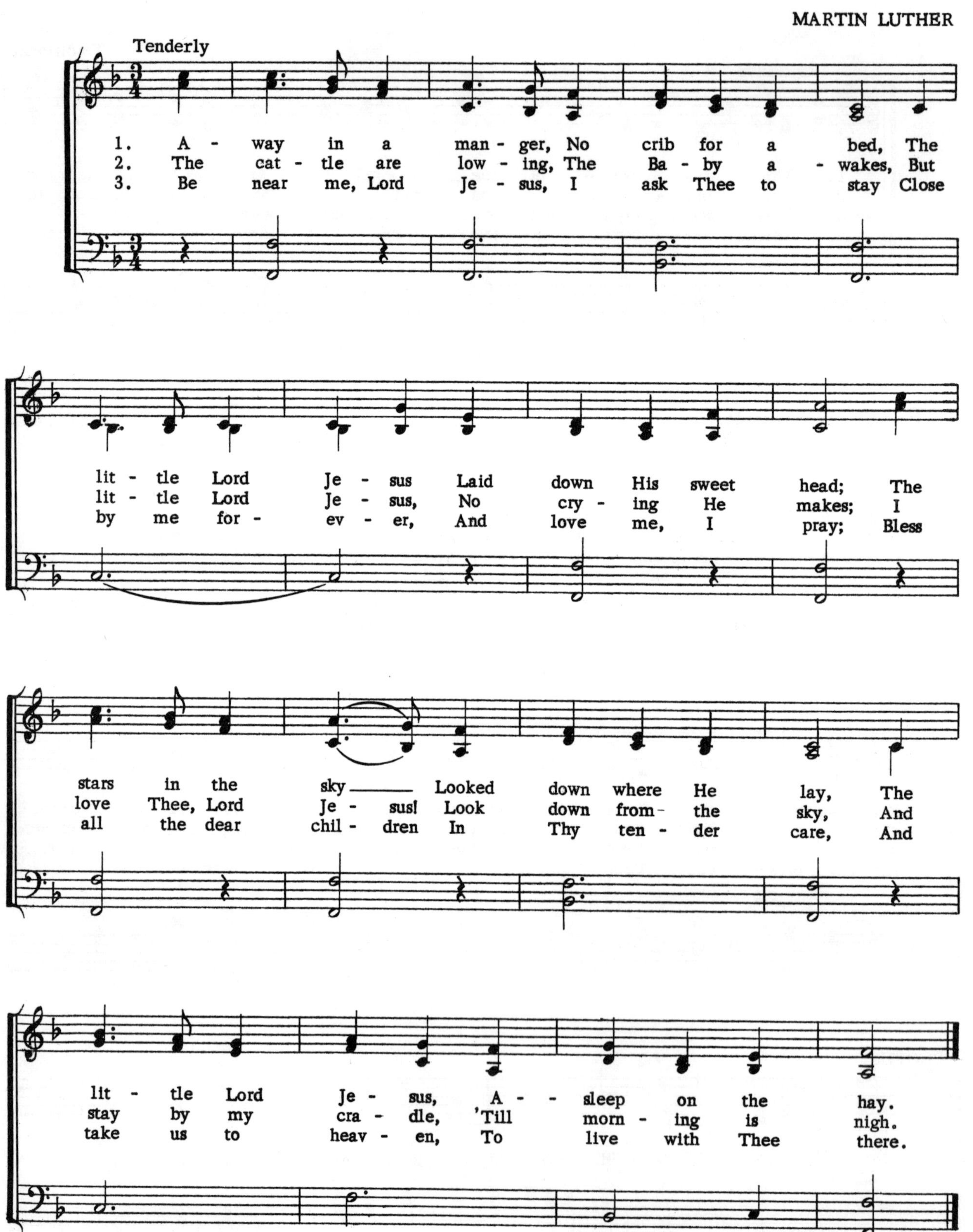
MARTIN LUTHER
Tenderly
1. A - way in a man - ger, No crib for a bed, The
2. The cat - tle are low - ing, The Ba - by a - wakes, But
3. Be near me, Lord Je - sus, I ask Thee to stay Close
lit - tle Lord Je - sus Laid down His sweet head; The
lit - tle Lord Je - sus, No cry - ing He makes; I
by me for - ev - er, And love me, I pray; Bless
stars in the sky Looked down where He lay, The
love Thee, Lord Je - sus! Look down from - the sky, And
all the dear chil - dren In Thy ten - der care, And
lit - tle Lord Je - sus, A - sleep on the hay.
stay by my cra - dle, 'Till morn - ing is nigh.
take us to heav - en, To live with Thee there.

God Rest You Merry, Gentlemen

Traditional
Arr. by Sir John Stainer

Lively.
mf
1. God rest you mer - ry, gen - tle - men, Let noth - ing you dis -
2. Now to the Lord sing prai - ses All you with - in this
may, Re - mem - ber Christ our Sa - vi - our Was born on Christ - mas
place, And with true love and broth - er - hood Each oth - er now em -
Day, To save us all from Sa - tan's pow'r When
brace; This ho - ly tide of Christ - mas All
we were gone a - stray;
oth - er doth de - face.
CHORUS
ff
O ti - dings of com - fort and
joy, com-fort and joy, O ti - dings of com - fort and joy.

We Three Kings of Orient Are

J. H. HOPKINS

Arr. by George Snowhill

Moderato
mf
1. We three kings of O - ri - ent are; bear - ing
2. Born a King on Beth - le - hem's plain, Gold I
3. Glor - ious now be - hold Him a - rise, King and
mf
gifts we tra - verse a - far field and foun - tain,
bring to crown Him a - gain, King for - ev - er,
God and sac - ri - fice, Al - le - lu - ia,
Moor and moun - tain, fol - low - ing yon - der star. O
ceas - ing nev - er, o - ver us all to reign. O
Al - le - lu - ia! Sounds through the earth and skies. O
Star of won - der, Star of night, Star with

roy - al beaut - y bright, West - ward lead - ing,
still pro - ceed - ing, guide us to Thy per - fect light.
Silent Night
Slowly
pp
Si - lent night! Ho - ly night! All is calm, all is bright Round you
Stil - le Nacht, Hei-li-ge Nacht! Al - les schläft, ein - sam wacht. Nur das
vir - gin moth- er and Child! Ho - ly In- fant, so ten - der and mild,
trau- te hoch - hei - li - ge - Paar, Hol - der Kna - be im lo - cki - gen Haar,
Sleep in heav - en - ly peace, Sleep in heav - en - ly peace.
Schlaf in himm-li-cher Ruh, Schlaf in himm-li-cher Ruh!
A - men.

The Twelve Days of Christmas

Arr. by George Snowhill

Tenderly with growing wonder
On the first day of Christ-mas my true love gave to me a
par - tridge in a pear tree.
On the sec - cond day of Christ - mas my
true love gave to me two tur -tle doves and a par-tridge in a pear - tree.
On the third day of Christ-mas my true love gave to me three French hens,
On the fourth day of Christ-mas my true love gave to me four col - ly birds;
two tur - tle doves and a par - tridge in a pear - tree.

On the fifth day of Christ-mas my true love gave to me five gold-en rings,
four col-ly birds, three French hens, two tur-tle doves, and a par-tridge in a pear tree.
On the sixth day of Christ-mas my true love gave to me six geese a-lay-ing,
On the sev-enth day of Christ-mas my true love gave to me se-ven swans a-swim-ming,
On the eighth day of Christ-mas my true love gave to me eight maids a-milk-ing,
On the ninth day of Christ-mas my true love gave to me nine pip-ers pip-ing
On the tenth day of Christ-mas my true love gave to me ten drum-mers drum-ming
On the lev-enth day of Christ-mas my true love gave to me 'lev-en Lords a-leap-ing
On the twelfth day of Christ-mas my true love gave to me twelve la-dies danc-ing
five gold-en rings, four col-ly birds, three French hens,
two tur-tle doves and a par-tridge in a pear-tree.

Deck the Halls

Welsh Air

Joyfully
1. Deck the halls with boughs of hol - ly!
2. See the blaz - ing Yule be-fore us, Fa la la la la la la la la
3. Fast a - way the old year pass - es,
'Tis the sea - son to be jol - ly,
Strike the harp and join the chor - us, Fa la la la la la la la la
Hail the new, ye lads and lass - es,
Don we now our gay ap - par - el,
Fol - low me in mer - ry meas - ure, Fa la la la la la la la la
Sing we joy - ous all to - geth - er,
Troll the an - cient Yule - tide car - ol,
While I tell of Yule - tide trea - sure, Fa la la la la la la la la.
Heed - less of the wind and weath - er,

Jingle Bells

Brightly
J. PIERPONT
1. Dash - ing thro' the snow In a one horse o - pen sleigh,
2. A day or two a - go I — thought I'd take a ride, And
3. Now the ground is white, Go it while you're young,
O'er the fields we go, Laugh-ing all the way; Bells on bob- tail ring,
soon Miss Fan- ny Bright Was seat -ed by my side;The horse was lean and lank, Mis-
Take the girls to - night, And sing this sleigh-ing song;Just get a bob-tailed nag Two-
Mak-ing spir - its bright; What fun it is to ride and sing A sleigh-ing song to-night!
for-tune seem'd his lot, He got in- to a drift- ed bank, And we, we got up- sot.
for - ty for his speed, Then hitch him to an o - pen sleigh, And crack! you'll take the lead.
CHORUS
Jin - gle bells! jin - gle bells! Jin - gle all the way! Oh! what fun it is to ride
1.
In a one - horse o - pen sleigh! —
2.
In a one - horse o - pen sleigh.

Good King Wenceslas

Arr. by Felix Guenther

In march tempo

1. Good King Wen - ces - las look'd out On the Feast of Ste - phen,
2. "Hith - er, page, and stand by me, If thou know'st it tell - ing
3. "Bring me flesh and bring me wine, Bring me pine logs hith - er,

When the snow lay round a - bout, Deep, and crisp and e - ven;
Yon - der peas - ant, who is he? Where, and what his dwell - ing?"
Thou and I will see him dine, When we bear them thith - er."

Bright - ly shone the moon that night, Though the frost was cru - el,
"Sire, he lives a good league hence, Un - der - neath the moun - tain;
Page and mon - arch, forth they went, On - ward both to - geth - er,

When a poor man came in sight, Gath - 'ring win - ter fu - el.
Right a - gainst the for - est fence, By St. Ag - nes' foun - tain."
Through the rude wind's wild la - ment, And the bit - ter weath - er.

4. "Sire, the night is darker now,
   And the storm blows stronger;
Fails my heart, I know not how,
   I can go no longer."
"Mark my footsteps, good my page,
   Tread thou in them boldly;
Thou shalt find the winter's rage
   Freeze thy blood less coldly."

5. In his master's steps he trod,
   Where the snow lay dinted;
Heat was in the very sod
   Which the saint had printed.
Therefore, Christian men, be sure,
   Wealth or rank possessing,
Ye who now will bless the poor,
   Shall yourself find blessing.

O Tannenbaum

Andante
mf
1. O hem - lock tree, O hem - lock tree how
2. O hem - lock tree, O hem - lock tree. in
3. O hem - lock tree, O hem - lock tree, a
O Tan - nen -baum, O Tan - nen -baum, wie
1.
2.
faith - ful are thy bran - ches! O branch - es! thou'rt
truth I dear - ly love thee. O love thee. How
les - son thou dost teach me, O teach me. That
treu sind dei - ne Blät - ter! O Blät - ter! Du
green when sum-mer breez - es blow, And green 'mid win - ter's drift - ing snow, O
oft at mer - ry Christ-mas-tide hast filled my heart with joy and pride, O
ev - er hope and con - stan- cy will strength and com - fort give to me, O
grünst nicht nur zur Som - mer-zeit, nein, auch im Win - ter wenn es schneit, O
hem - lock tree, O hem -lock tree, How faith - ful are thy branch - es.
hem - lock tree, O hem - lock tree, In truth I dear - ly love thee.
hem - lock tree, O hem - lock tree, A les - son thou dost teach me.
Tan -nen-baum, O Tan - nen - baum, wie treu sind dei - ne Blät - ter.

A Mighty Fortress Is Our God

By MARTIN LUTHER

Arr. by L. Anthony

Andante deciso
1. A mighty - y for - tress is our God, A
2. Did we in our own strength con - fide, our
3. And though this world, with dev - ils filled, should
4. That word a - bove all earth - ly pow'rs, no
bul - wark nev - er fail - ing; Our Help - er He a -
striv - ing would be los - ing; Were not the right man
threat - en to un - do us; We will not fear, For
thanks to them a - bid - eth; The spi - rit and the
mid the flood of mor - tal ills pre - vail - ing. For
on our side, the man of God's own choos - ing. Dost
God hath willed His truth to tri - umph through us. The
gifts are ours, through Him who with us sid - eth, Let
still our an - cient foe Doth seek to work us woe; his
ask who that may be? Christ Je - sus, it is He! Lord
prince of dark - ness grim, we trem - ble not for him; His
goods and kin - dred go, This mor - tal life al - so;, The

craft and pow'r are great, and armed with cru - el hate on
Sab - a - oth His name, From age to age the same, and
rage we can en - dure, for lo! his doom is sure, one
bod - y they may kill; God's truth a - bid - eth still, His
earth is not his e - qual.
He must win the bat - tle.
lit - tle word shall fell him.
king - dom is for - ev - er. A - men.

Now the Day Is Over

Words by SABINE BARING-GOULD

Andante

Music by J. BARNBY

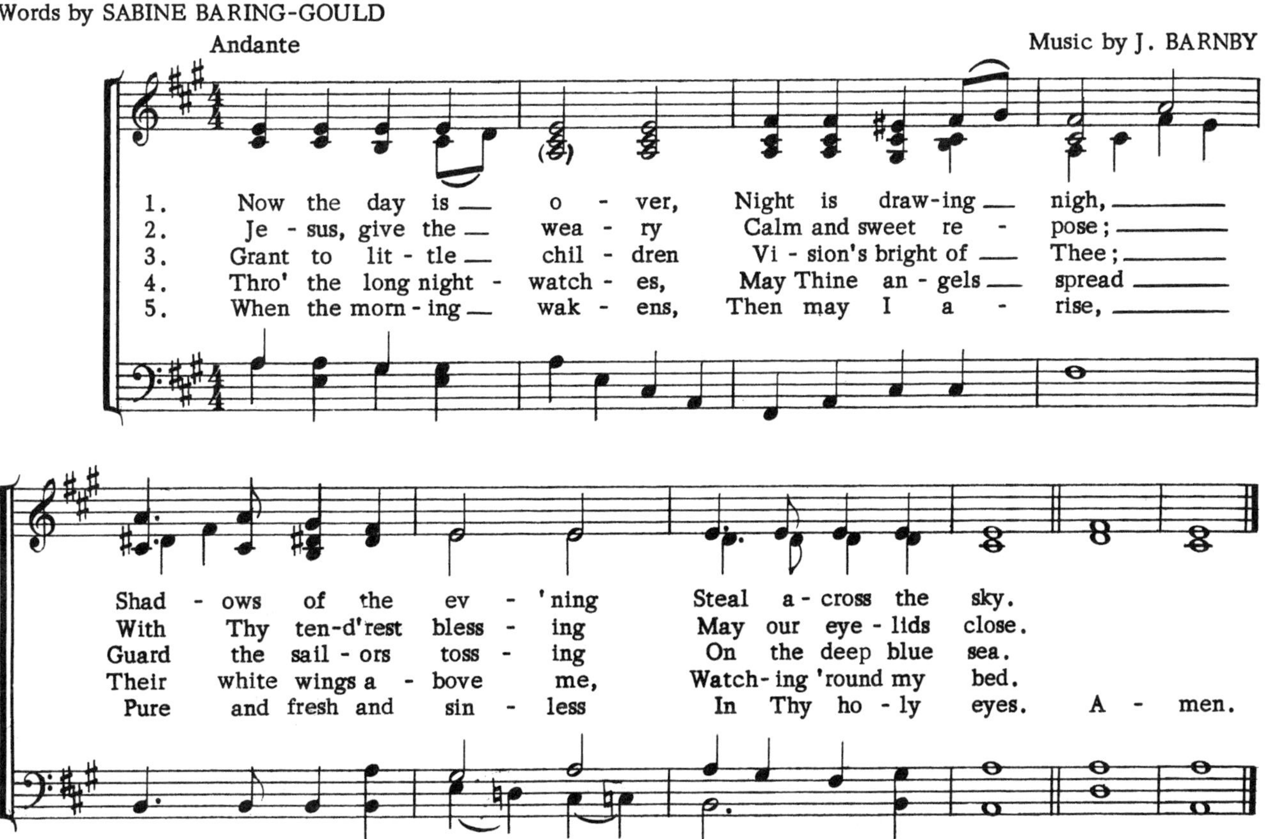
1. Now the day is o - ver, Night is draw-ing nigh,
2. Je - sus, give the wea - ry Calm and sweet re - pose;
3. Grant to lit - tle chil - dren Vi - sion's bright of Thee;
4. Thro' the long night - watch - es, May Thine an - gels spread
5. When the morn - ing wak - ens, Then may I a - rise,
Shad - ows of the ev - 'ning Steal a - cross the sky.
With Thy ten-d'rest bless - ing May our eye - lids close.
Guard the sail - ors toss - ing On the deep blue sea.
Their white wings a - bove me, Watch - ing 'round my bed.
Pure and fresh and sin - less In Thy ho - ly eyes. A - men.

Abide with Me

H. F. LYTE

W. H. MONK

Slow tempo
1. A - bide with me: fast falls the e - ven - tide;
2. Swift to its close ebbs out life's lit - tle day;
3. I need Thy pres - ence ev - 'ry pass - ing hour:
4. Hold Thou Thy cross be - fore my clos - ing eyes,
The dark - ness deep - ens; Lord, with me a - bide:
Earth's joys grow dim, its glo - ries pass a - way,
What but Thy grace can foil the tempt - er's pow'r?
Shine thro' the gloom, and point me to the skies:
When oth - er help - ers fail, and com - forts flee,
Change and de - cay in all a - round I see:
Who like Thy - self my guide and stay can be?
Heav'n's morn - ing breaks, and earth's vain shad - ows flee
Help of the help - less, O a - bide with me!
O Thou who chang - est not, a - bide with me!
Through cloud and sun - shine, O a - bide with me!
In life, in death, O Lord, a - bide with me!

Jesus Loves Me

Moderato
1. Je - sus loves me! this I know, For the Bi - ble tells me so; Lit - tle ones to Him be - long, They are weak, but He is strong.
2. Je - sus loves me! He who died, Heav - en's gates to o - pen wide; He will wash a - way my sin, Let His lit - tle child come in.
3. Je - sus loves me! He will stay Close be - side me all the way; If I love Him when I die, He will take me home on High.
Yes, Je - sus loves me, Yes, Je - sus loves me,
Yes, Je - sus loves me, The Bi - ble tells me so

Bringing in the Sheaves

KNOWLES SHAW
GEORGE A. MINOR
Moderato
1. Sow - ing in the morn - ing, sow - ing seeds of kind - ness,
2. Sow - ing in the sun - shine, sow - ing in the shad - ows,
3. Go - ing forth with weep - ing, sow - ing for the Mas - ter,
Sow - ing in the noon - tide and the dew- y eve; Wait- ing for the har - vest,
Fear- ing nei- ther clouds nor win - ter's chill-ing breeze; By and by the har - vest,
Tho' the loss sus - tained our spir- it oft - en grieves; When our weep-ing's o - ver,
and the time of reap - ing, We shall come re -joic - ing, bring-ing in the sheaves.
and the la - bor end - ed, We shall come re -joic - ing, bring-ing in the sheaves.
He will bid us wel - come, We shall come re -joic - ing, bring-ing in the sheaves.
CHORUS
1.
Bring-ing in the sheaves, bring- ing in the sheaves, We shall come re - joic - ing,
bring - ing in the sheaves; We shall come re - joic - ing, bring- ing in the sheaves.

For the Beauty of the Earth

Words by F. S. PIERPONT

C. KOCHER
Arr. by George Snowhill

Not too slow

1. For the beau - ty of the earth, For the glor - y of the skies,
2. For the won - der of each hour of the day and of the night,

For the love which from our birth o - ver and a - round us lies.
Hill and vale and trees and flow'r, Sun and moon, and stars of light;

CHORUS

Lord of all, to Thee we raise This our hymn of greate-ful praise.

Praise God from Whom All Blessings Flow

Arr. by George Snowhill
With spirit
Praise God, from Whom all bless - ings flow; Praise Him, all creatures here be-low; Praise
Him a - bove, ye heav' nly host; Praise Fa - ther, Son, and Ho - ly Ghost.

Now Thank We All Our God

J. CRUGER
Arr. by George Snowhill

Majestically
1. Now thank we all our God, With hearts and hands and voic - es, With wond - rous things hath done, In whom this world re - joic - es, Who from our moth - er's arms hath blessed us on our way with count - less gifts of love, and still is ours to - day.
2. O may this bount-eous God through all our life be near us, With ev - er joy - ful hearts, and bless - ed peace to cheer us; And keep us in His grace, and guide us when per - plexed, and free us from all ills in this world and the next.
3. All praise and thanks to God the Fath - er now be giv - en, The Son and Him who reigns with Them in high - est hea - ven; The one e - tern - al God, Whom earth and heav'n a - dore; for thus it was, is now, and shall be ev - er - more. A - men.

God Be with You Till We Meet Again

J. E. RANKIN
Andante
W. G. TOMER
1. God be with you till we meet a - gain; By His coun-sels guide, up - hold you,
2. God be with you till we meet a - gain; 'Neath His wings pro-tect-ing hide you,
3. God be with you till we meet a - gain; When life's per-ils thick con - found you,
With His sheep se - cure - ly fold you; God be with you till we meet a - gain.
Dai - ly man - na still pro - vide you; God be with you till we meet a - gain.
Put His arms un - fail - ing 'round you; God be with you till we meet a - gain.
CHORUS
Till we meet, till we meet, Till we meet at Je - sus' feet; Till we
Till we meet, till we meet, till we meet;
meet, till we meet, God be with you till we meet a - gain.
Till we meet, till we meet,

Rocked in the Cradle of the Deep

By JOSEPH P. KNIGHT

Andante
1. Rock'd in the cra - dle of the deep,_ I lay me down_ in peace to sleep; Se -
2. And such the trust that still were mine,_ Tho' storm-y winds_ sweep o'er the brine, Or
cure I rest up - on the wave,_ For Thou, O Lord,_ hast pow'r to save. I
though the tem-pest's fier-y breath,_ Roused me from sleep_ to wreck and death. In
know Thou wilt not slight my call, For Thou dost mark the spar-row's fall!
o - cean's wave still safe with Thee, The germ of im - mor-tal - i - ty;
And
calm and peace-ful is my sleep, Rock'd in the cra-dle of the deep, And
rit.
calm and peace-ful is my sleep, Rock'd in the cra-dle of the deep.
rit.

Come, Thou Almighty King

Stately

FELICE De GIARDINI

1. Come, Thou Al - might - y King, Help us Thy name to sing,
2. Come, Thou In - car - nate Word, Gird on Thy might - y sword,
3. To the great One in Three E - ter - nal prais - es be

Help us to praise: Fa - ther, all glo - ri - ous, O'er all vic -
Our pray'r at - tend: Come, and Thy peo - ple bless, And give Thy
Hence ev - er - more. His sov - 'reign maj - es - ty May we in

to - ri - ous, Come, and reign o - ver us, An - cient of Days.
word suc - cess: Spir - it of ho - li - ness, On us de - scend.
glo - ry see, And to e - ter - ni - ty, Love and a - dore.

O God, Our Help in Ages Past

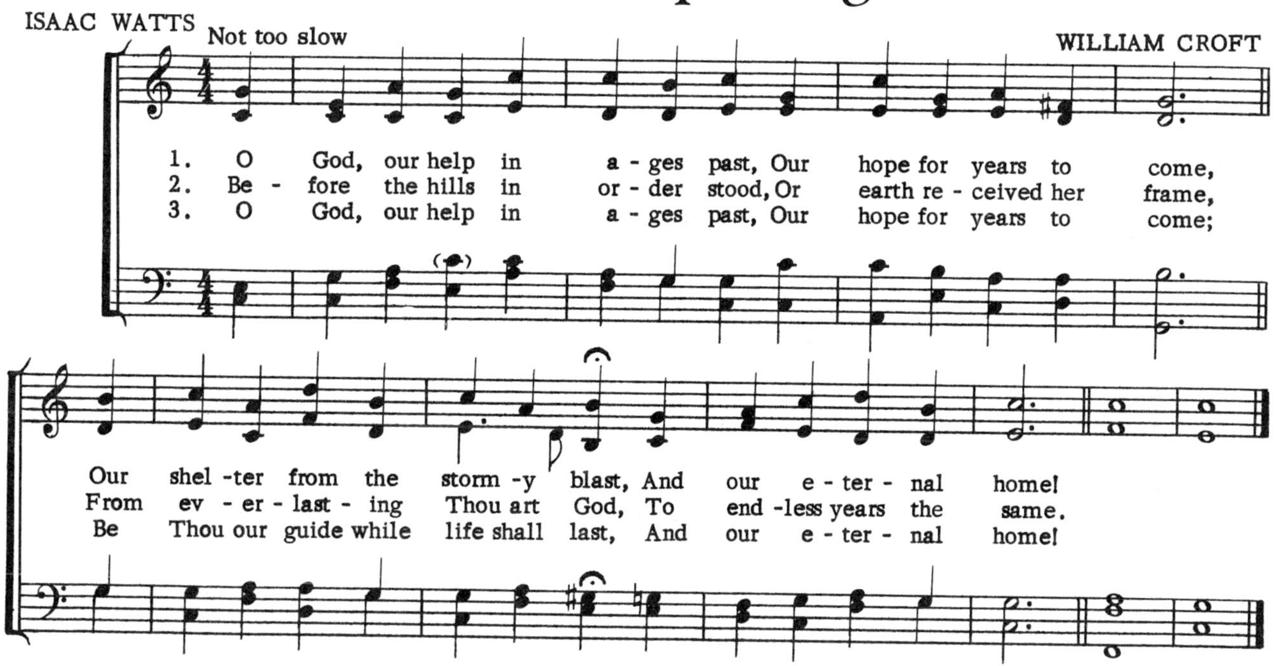
ISAAC WATTS
Not too slow
WILLIAM CROFT
1. O God, our help in a - ges past, Our hope for years to come,
2. Be - fore the hills in or - der stood, Or earth re - ceived her frame,
3. O God, our help in a - ges past, Our hope for years to come;
Our shel - ter from the storm - y blast, And our e - ter - nal home!
From ev - er - last - ing Thou art God, To end - less years the same.
Be Thou our guide while life shall last, And our e - ter - nal home!

Rock of Ages

AUGUSTUS M. TOPLADY — THOMAS HASTINGS

Andante

1. Rock of A - ges, cleft for me, Let me hide my - self in Thee; Let the wa - ter and the blood, From Thy wound - ed side which flowed, Be of sin the dou - ble cure, Save from wrath and make me pure.
2. Could my tears for - ev - er flow, Could my zeal no lan - guor know, These for sin could not a - tone; Thou must save, and Thou a - lone; In my hand no price I bring, Sim - ply to Thy cross I cling.
3. While I draw this fleet - ing breath, When my eyes shall close in death, When I rise to worlds un - known, And be - hold Thee on Thy throne, Rock of A - ges, cleft for me, Let me hide my - self in Thee.

Work, for the Night is Coming

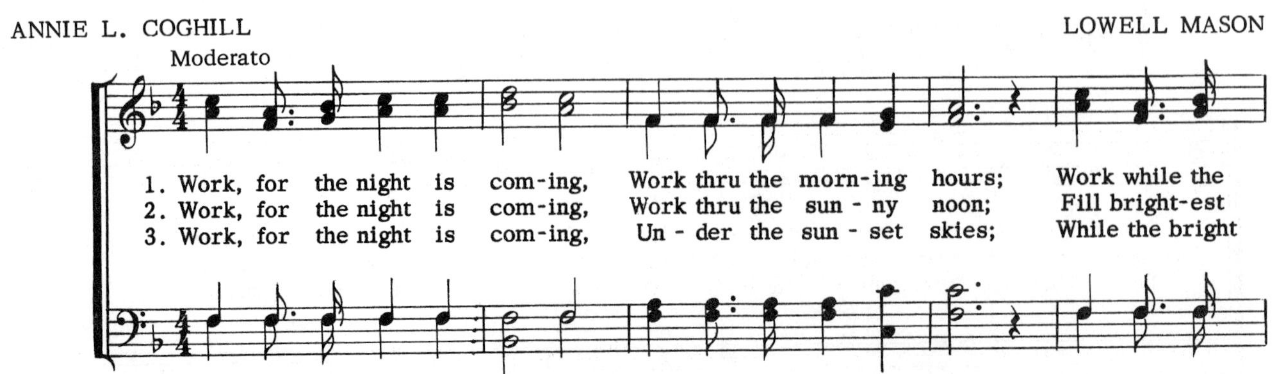
ANNIE L. COGHILL
LOWELL MASON
Moderato
1. Work, for the night is com-ing, Work thru the morn-ing hours; Work while the
2. Work, for the night is com-ing, Work thru the sun - ny noon; Fill bright-est
3. Work, for the night is com-ing, Un - der the sun - set skies; While the bright

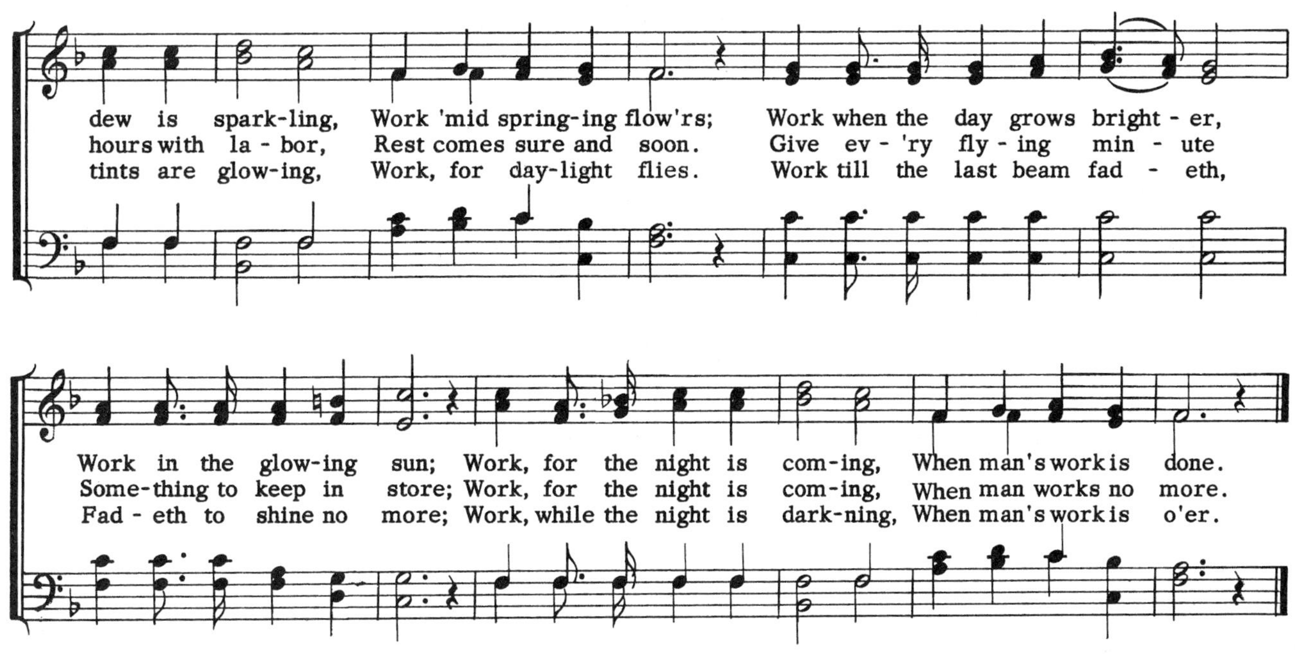
dew is spark-ling, Work 'mid spring-ing flow'rs; Work when the day grows bright - er,
hours with la - bor, Rest comes sure and soon. Give ev - 'ry fly - ing min - ute
tints are glow-ing, Work, for day-light flies. Work till the last beam fad - eth,
Work in the glow-ing sun; Work, for the night is com-ing, When man's work is done.
Some-thing to keep in store; Work, for the night is com-ing, When man works no more.
Fad - eth to shine no more; Work, while the night is dark-ning, When man's work is o'er.

Holy, Holy, Holy

REGINALD HEBER

Rev. JOHN B. DYKES

Stately

1. Ho-ly, Ho-ly, Ho - ly, Lord God Al - might - y! Ear - ly in the
2. Ho-ly, Ho-ly, Ho - ly! All the saints a - dore Thee, Cast - ing down their
3. Ho-ly, Ho-ly, Ho - ly, Lord God Al - might - y! All Thy works shall

morn - ing our song shall rise to Thee; Ho - ly, Ho - ly, Ho - ly!
golden crowns a - round the glass-y sea; Cher - u - bim and ser - a - phim
praise Thy name in earth, and sky, and sea; Ho - ly, Ho - ly, Ho - ly!

Mer - ci - ful and Might - y! God in Three Per-sons, bless-ed Trin - i - ty!
fall - ing down be - fore Thee, Who wert, and art, and ev - er-more shalt be.
Mer - ci - ful and Might - y! God in Three Per-sons, bless-ed Trin - i - ty!

Lead, Kindly Light

J. H. NEWMAN
Moderato
J. B. DYKES
1. Lead, kind - ly Light, a - mid th'en - cir - cling gloom, Lead Thou me on; The night is dark, and I am far from home;__ Lead Thou me on.__ Keep Thou my feet; I do not ask to see.__ The dis - tant scene one step e - nough__ for me.__
2. I was not ev - er thus, nor prayed that Thou Shouldst lead me on; I loved to choose and see my path; but now__ Lead Thou me on.__ I loved the gar - ish day, and spite of fears,__ Pride ruled my will: Re - mem -ber not__ past years.__
3. So long Thy pow'r has blest me, sure it still Will lead me on O'er moor and fen, o'er crag and tor- ent, till__ The night is gone.__ And with the morn those an - gel- fac - es smile,__ Which I have loved long since, and lost__ a - while.__
A - men.

Nearer, My God, to Thee

SARAH F. ADAMS
Arr. by Lowell Mason
Not too fast
1. Near - er, my God, to Thee, Near - er to Thee! E'en though it be a cross That rais - eth me; Still all my song shall be,
2. Though like the wan - der - er, The sun gone down, Dark - ness be o - ver me, My rest a stone; Yet in my dreams I'd be
3. There let the way ap - pear, Steps un - to heav'n: All that Thou send - est me, In mer - cy giv'n: An - gels to beck - on me,
Near - er, my God, to Thee, Near - er, my God, to Thee, Near - er, to Thee!
Glory Be to the Father
Ancient Hymn
HENRY W. GREATOREX
Stately
Glo-ry be to the Fa-ther, and to the Son, and to the Ho-ly Ghost; As it was in the be - gin- ing, is now, and ev-er shall be, world with-out end. A - men, A - men.

Dear Lord and Father of Mankind

JOHN G. WHITTIER

FREDERICK C. MAKER

Andante

1. Dear Lord and Fa - ther of man - kind, For - give our fev - 'rish
2. In sim - ple trust, like theirs who heard, Be - side the Syr - ian
3. Breathe thro' the heats of our de - sire Thy cool - ness and Thy

ways! Re - clothe us in our right - ful mind; In pur - er lives Thy
sea, The gra - cious call - ing of the Lord, Let us, like them, with-
balm; Let sense be dumb, let flesh re - tire: Speak thro' the earth - quake,

ser - vice find, In deep - er rev - 'rence, praise.
out a word, Rise up and fol - low Thee.
wind and fire, O still small voice of calm!

Softly Now the Light of Day

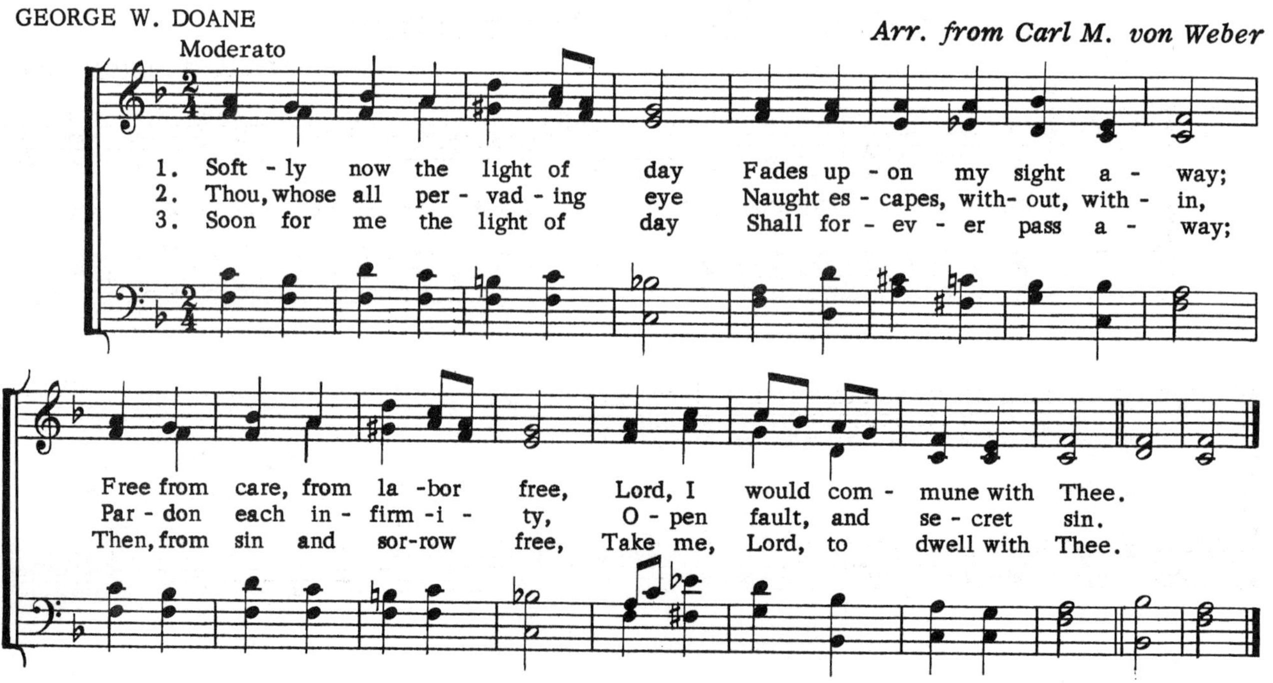
GEORGE W. DOANE
Arr. from Carl M. von Weber
Moderato
1. Soft - ly now the light of day Fades up - on my sight a - way;
2. Thou, whose all per - vad - ing eye Naught es - capes, with- out, with - in,
3. Soon for me the light of day Shall for - ev - er pass a - way;
Free from care, from la - bor free, Lord, I would com - mune with Thee.
Par - don each in - firm - i - ty, O - pen fault, and se - cret sin.
Then, from sin and sor-row free, Take me, Lord, to dwell with Thee.

Faith of Our Fathers

FREDERICK W. FABER

H. F. HEMY

Andante
1. Faith of our fa - thers! liv - ing still
2. Our fa - thers, chained in pris - ons dark,
3. Faith of our fa - thers! we will love
In spite of dun - geon, fire and sword: O how our
Were still in heart and con - science free: How sweet would
Both friend and foe in all our strife: And preach thee,
hearts beat high with joy When- e'er we hear that
be their child - ren's fate, If they, like them, could
too, as love knows how, By kind - ly words and
glo - rious word! Faith of our fa - thers! ho - ly
die for Thee! Faith of our fa - thers! ho - ly
vir - tuous life: Faith of our fa - thers! ho - ly
faith! We will be true to Thee till death!
faith! We will be true to Thee till death!
faith! We will be true to Thee till death!

The Star Spangled Banner

FRANCIS SCOTT KEY

Majestically
O — say! can you see, — by the dawn's ear - ly
On the shore, dim - ly seen — thro' the mists of the
O — thus be it ev - er when — free men shall
light, What so proud - ly we hailed at the twi - light's last
deep, Where the foe's haugh - ty host in dread si - lence re-
stand Be - tween their loved homes and the war's de - so -
gleam - ing? Whose broad stripes and bright stars thru the per - il - ous
pos - es, What is that which the breeze, o'er the tow - er - ing
la - tion! Blest with vic - t'ry and peace, may the heav'n res - cued
fight, O'er the ram - parts we watched, were so gal - lant - ly
steep, As it fit - ful - ly blows, half con - ceals, half dis-
land Praise the Pow'r that hath made and pre - served us a

stream - ing? And the rock - et's red glare the bombs burst - ing in
- clos - es? Now it catch - es the gleam of the morn - ing's first
na - tion! Then con - quer we must, when our cause it is
air, Gave proof thro' the night that our flag was still there.
beam, In full glo - ry re flect - ed now shines on the stream;
just, And this be our mot - to: "In God is our trust!"
O say, does that Star - span - gled Ban - ner yet
'Tis the Star - span - gled Ban - ner, O long may it
And the Star - span - gled Ban - ner in tri - umph shall
wave, O'er the land of the free and the home of the brave?
wave, O'er the land of the free and the home of the brave!
wave, O'er the land of the free and the home of the brave!

America
(MY COUNTRY, 'TIS OF THEE)

SAMUEL FRANCIS SMITH
HENRY CAREY
Maestoso
My coun - try, 'tis of thee, Sweet land of
My na - tive coun - try, thee, Land of the
Let mu - sic swell the breeze And ring from
Our fa - thers' God, to Thee, Au - thor of
lib - er - ty, Of thee I sing. Land where my
no - ble free, Thy name I love. I love thy
all the trees Sweet free - dom's song. Let mor - tal
lib - er - ty To Thee we sing. Long may our
fa - thers died! Land of the Pil - grims' pride!
rocks and rills, Thy woods and tem - pled hills;
tongues a - wake; Let all that breathe par - take;
land be bright With free - dom's ho - ly light;
From ev - 'ry moun - tain side Let free - dom ring!
My heart with rap - ture thrills Like that a - bove.
Let rocks their si - lence break, The sound pro - long.
Pro - tect us by Thy might, Great God, our King!

America the Beautiful

KATHERINE LEE BATES
SAMUEL A. WARD
Arr. by Harry Henneman
Stately
1. O beau - ti - ful for spa - cious skies, For am - ber waves of
2. O beau - ti - ful for pil - grim feet whose stern im - pas- sion'd
3. O beau - ti - ful for pa - triot dream That sees be- yond the
grain, For pur - ple moun - tain maj - es - ties a -
stress, A thor - ough - fare for free - dom beat a -
years Thine al - a - bas - ter cit - ies gleam un -
bove the fruit - ed plain. A - mer - i - ca! A -
cross the wil - der - ness. A - mer - i - ca! A -
dimmed by hu - man tears. A - mer - i - ca! A -
mer - i - ca! God shed His grace on thee, And
mer - i - ca! God mend thine ev - 'ry flaw, Con -
mer - i - ca! God shed His grace on thee, And
crown thy good with broth - er - hood from sea to shin - ing sea.
firm thy soul in self - con -trol, Thy lib - er - ty in law.
crown thy good with broth - er - hood from sea to shin - ing sea.

Hail Columbia

Words by JOSEPH HOPKINSON

Music by J. FAYLES

Marziale.
cresc.
f
1. Hail, Co - lum - bia, hap - py land! Hail, ye he - roes!
2. Im - mor - tal pa - triots! rise once more, De - fend your rights, de -
3. Be - hold the Chief who now com - mands, Once more to serve his
cresc.
heav'n - born band! Who fought and bled in Free - dom's cause, Who
fend your shore; Let no rude foe with im - pious hand, Let
coun - try stands, The rock on which the storm will beat, The
fought and bled in Free - dom's cause, And when the storm of war was gone, En -
no rude foe with im - pious hand, In - vade the shrine where sa - cred lies, Of
rock on which the storm will beat; But armed in vir - tue, firm and true, His
3
3
3
joyed the peace your val - or won. Let in - de - pend - ence
toil and blood the well - earned prize. While off - 'ring peace, sin -
hopes are fixed on heav'n and you. When hope was sink - ing

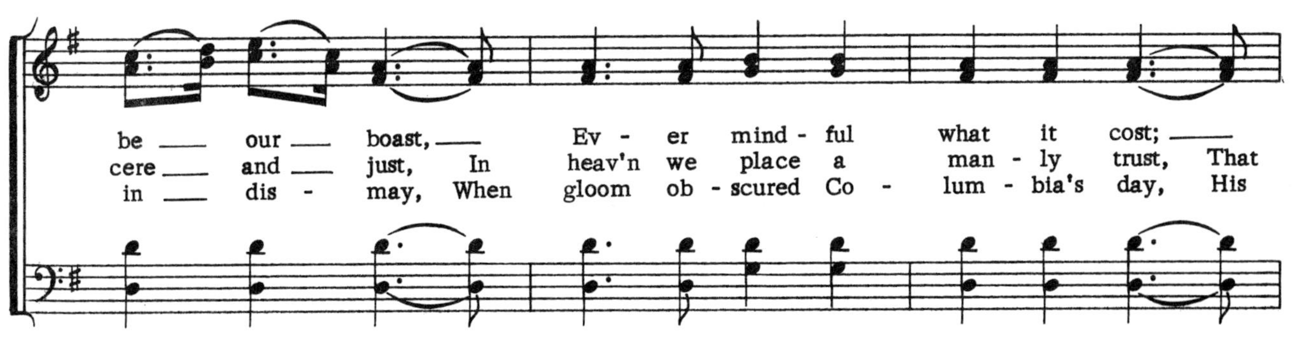
be — our — boast, — Ev - er mind - ful what it cost; —
cere — and — just, In heav'n we place a man - ly trust, That
in — dis - may, When gloom ob - scured Co - lum - bia's day, His

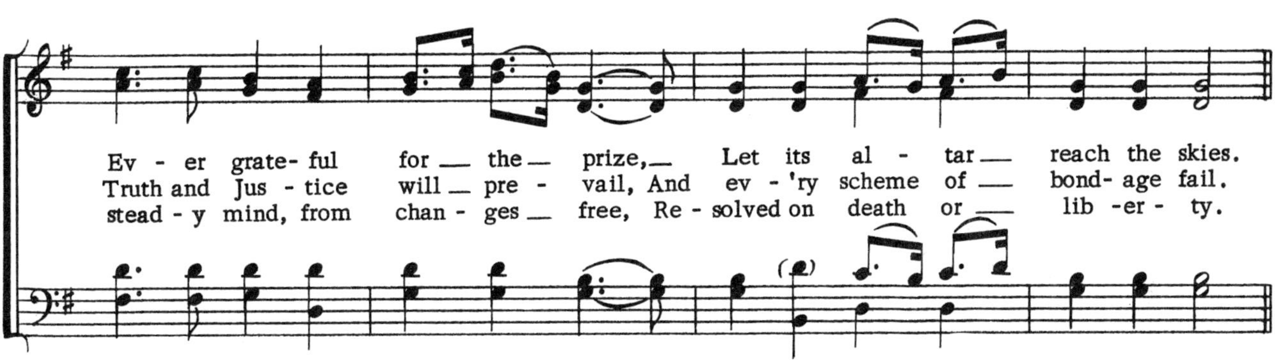
Ev - er grate- ful for — the — prize, — Let its al - tar — reach the skies.
Truth and Jus - tice will — pre - vail, And ev - 'ry scheme of — bond- age fail.
stead - y mind, from chan - ges — free, Re - solved on death or — lib - er - ty.

CHORUS
con forza.
Firm, u - ni - ted, let — us — be, Rally- ing 'round our lib - er - ty;

As a band of — broth - ers — joined, Peace — and — safe - ty we shall find.

Dixie

DAN EMMETT

With animation
I wish I was in the land of cot - ton, Old times there are
In Dix- ie Land where I was born in, Ear - ly on one
not for - got - ten, Look a - way! Look a - way! Look a - way! Dix- ie Land.
frost - y morn- in', Look a - way! Look a - way! Look a - way! Dix- ie Land.
CHORUS
Then I wish I was in Dix - ie, Hoo - ray! Hoo - ray! In Dix -ie Land, I'll
take my stand, To live and die in Dix - ie. A - way, A - way, A -
way down south in Dix- ie; A - way, A - way, A - way down south in Dix- ie.

Columbia, the Gem of the Ocean

Marcia
1. O Co - lum-bia! the gem of the o-cean, The home of the brave and the free,– The
2. When – war winged its wide de - so - la - tion, And threat-ened the land to de - form,– The
3. The – star-spang-led ban-ner bring hi - ther, O'er Co-lum-bia's true sons let it wave; may the
shrine of each pa-triot's de - vo-tion, A world of-fers home-age to thee Thy
ark then of free-dom's foun - da-tion, Co - lum - bia rode safe – the storm; With
wreaths they have won nev - er with-er,– Nor its stars cease to shine – on the brave. May the
man-dates make he-roes as - sem-ble,– When – lib - er - ty's form stands in view, Thy
gar-lands of vic - t'ry a - round her – When so proud-ly she bore – her brave crew, The
ser - vice un - it-ed ne'er sev - er,– But – hold to their col - ors so true; The
ban-ners make ty - ran-ny trem-ble When borne by the Red, White and Blue. When
flag proud-ly float - ing be-fore her. The boast of the Red, White and Blue. The
Ar - my and Na - vy for - ev - er! Three cheers for the Red, White and Blue. Three

borne by the Red, White and Blue, When borne by the Red, White and Blue, Thy
boast of the Red, White and Blue, The boast of the Red, White and Blue, The
cheers for the Red, White and Blue, Three cheers for the Red, White and Blue, The
ban - ners make ty - ran - ny trem - ble— When borne by the Red, White and Blue.
flag proud - ly float - ing be - fore her,— The boast of the Red, White and Blue.
Ar - my and Na - vy for - ev - er!— Three cheers for the Red, White and Blue.

The Marines' Hymn

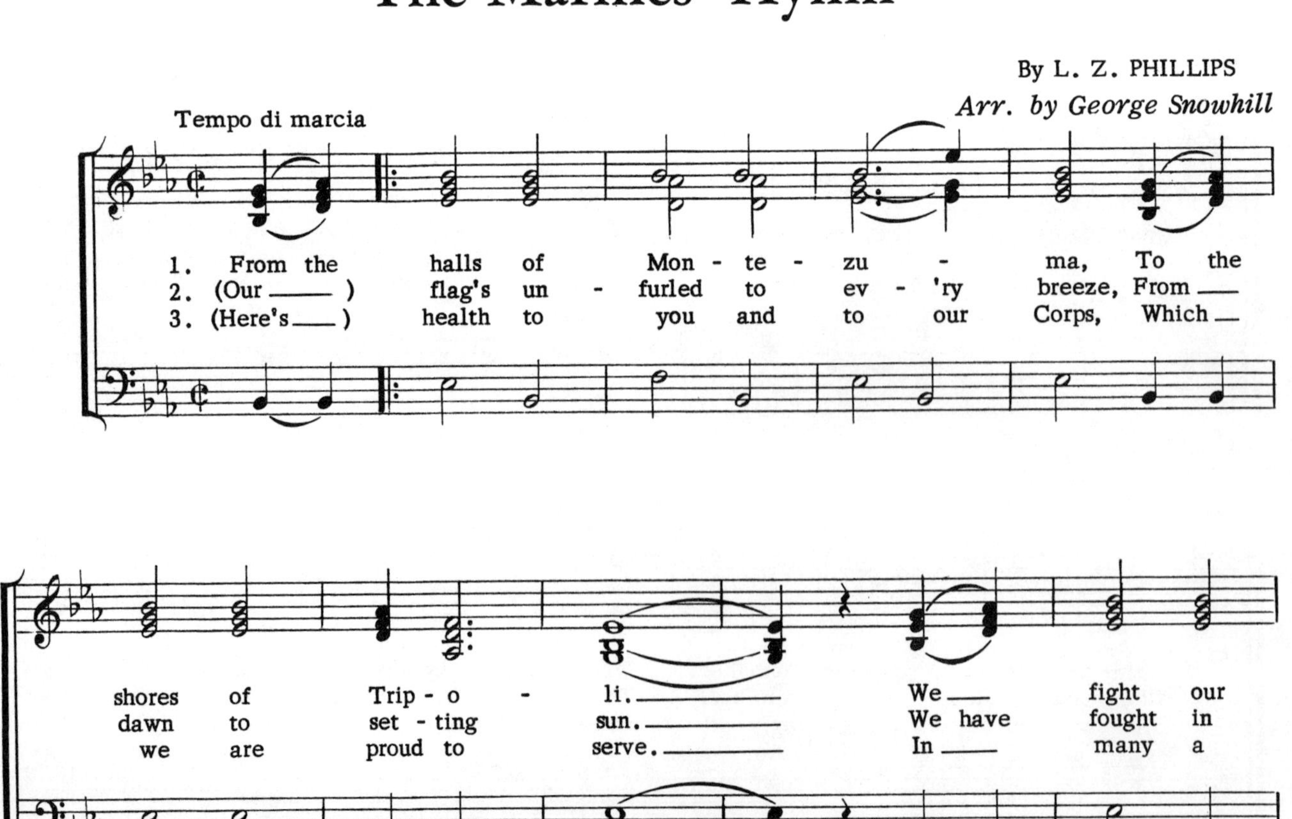
By L. Z. PHILLIPS
Arr. by George Snowhill
Tempo di marcia
1. From the halls of Mon - te - zu - ma, To the
2. (Our ——) flag's un - furled to ev - 'ry breeze, From ——
3. (Here's ——) health to you and to our Corps, Which ——
shores of Trip - o - li. —— We —— fight our
dawn to set - ting sun. —— We have fought in
we are proud to serve. —— In —— many a

Coun - try's bat - tles, On the land as on the
ev - 'ry clime and place, Where we could take a
strife we've fought for life, And nev - er lost our
sea. Ad - mi - ra - tion of the na -
gun, In the snow of far off north ern
nerve. If the Arm - y and the Na -
- tion, We're the fin - est ev - er seen, And we
lands, And in sun - ny trop - ic scenes, You will
- vy, Ev - er look on heav - en's scenes, They will
glo - ry in the ti - tle of "U - NI - TED
al - ways find us on the job the "U - NI - TED
find the streets are guard - ed by the "U - NI - TED
Last time
To Trio
STATES MA - RINES." 2. Our RINES."
STATES MA - RINES." 3. Here's RINES."
STATES MA - RINES." RINES."

Yankee Doodle

Allegro con brio
1. Fath'r and I went down to camp, A - long with Cap - tain Good - 'in, And there we saw the men and boys As thick as has - ty pud - din'
2. And there we saw a thous - and men, As rich as Squire Da - vid; And what they wast - ed ev - 'ry day I wish it could be sav - ed.
3. And there was Cap - tain Wash - ing - ton Up - on a slap - ping stal - lion, A - giv - ing or - ders to his men; I guess there was a mil - lion.
Yan - kee Doo - dle keep it up, Yan - kee Doo - dle dan - dy,
cresc. al f
Mind the mu - sic and the step, And with the girls be han - dy.

Battle Hymn of the Republic

JULIA WARD HOWE

Air, "John Brown's Body."

Allegretto
1. Mine eyes have seen the glo - ry of the com- ing of the Lord; He is
2. I have seen Him in the watch-fires of a hun -dred cir -cling camps; They have
3. He has sound-ed forth the trum-pet that shall nev- er call re - treat; He is
4. In the beau -ty of the lil - ies, Christ was born a - cross the sea, With a
tramp - ling out the vin - tage where the grapes of wrath are stored; He hath
build - ed Him an al - tar in the eve - ning dews and damps; I can
sift - ing out the hearts of men be - fore His judg -ment seat; Oh, be
glo - ry in His bos - om that trans - fig - ures you and me; As He
loosed the fate- ful light-ning of His ter - ri - ble swift sword, His truth is march-ing on.
read His right-eous sen-tence by the dim and flar- ing lamps, His day is march-ing on.
swift, my soul, to an - swer Him! be ju - bi -lant, my feet! Our God is march-ing on.
died to make men ho - ly, let us die to make men free, While God is march-ing on.
CHORUS Con spirito
f
Glo - ry! glo - ry! Hal- le - lu - jah! Glo - ry! glo- ry! Hal- le - lu - jah!
Glo - ry! glo - ry! Hal -le - lu - jah! His truth is march-ing on.

When Johnny Comes Marching Home

LOUIS LAMBERT
Arr. by G. M. Groene

With spirit.
Solo or Unison
CHORUS
When John- ny comes march-ing home a - gain, Hur - rah, Hur - rah!
The old church bell will peal with joy, Hur - rah, Hur - rah!
Get read - y then for the ju - bi - lee, Hur - rah, Hur - rah!
CHORUS
We'll give him a heart - y wel - come then, Hur - rah, Hur - rah!
To wel - come our dar - ling boy a - gain, Hur - rah, Hur - rah!
We'll give the he - roes three times three, Hur - rah, Hur - rah!
Solo
The men will cheer, The boys will shout, The la - dies, they will all turn out,
The vil - lage lads and las - sies gay With ros - es, they will strew the way,
The lau - rel wreath is read - y now To place up - on his loy - al brow,
CHORUS
And we'll all feel gay When John - ny comes march - ing home.

Index of First Lines

Index of Titles

INVITATION TO THE PIANO

by

ARNOLD BROIDO and FELIX GREISSLE

with a Foreword by

IRWIN FREUNDLICH

Juilliard School of Music

THE UNIVERSITY SOCIETY, Inc.

Educational Publishers since 1897

NEW YORK

1962

Foreword

In these days piano lessons must also be music lessons. The intelligent teacher tries to nurture the student by feeding him simple but basic musical ideas that will stand him in good stead in his later studies. The mechanical drudgery of meaningless repetition no longer passes for genuine learning, and in its place has come the adoption of interesting musical materials tastefully presented for the young student.

What better way to appeal to young people than through the music they know? What better way than through the folk and traditional songs that are part and parcel of their heritage? Many such collections exist, since modern piano teaching has, for many years, recognized the fruitfulness of using such materials in the early stages of learning.

The value of the present collection lies in the settings skillfully adapted to the early grades and in the variety of songs chosen. The settings carefully avoid excessive difficulties and, at the same time, highlight basic problems that the youngster must and can master with ease. Phrasing, touch problems, proper stress, tempo, chord playing, melody with accompaniment, and simple counterpoint are all to be found herein.

I find this "INVITATION TO THE PIANO" a most welcome and useful addition to the teaching materials now available for the early grades.

IRWIN FREUNDLICH
Juilliard School of Music

THE UNIVERSITY SOCIETY INC.
FOUNDED 1897

Manufactured in the U.S.A.

CONTENTS

FOLK SONG

FOLK SONG
1 1 2 3 4 3 2 3 2 1
In the morn-ing comes the dawn, Sun comes up, night is gone!

Teach: R.H. 5 finger position;
fingering numbers; $\frac{4}{4}$; ,

Czech Song

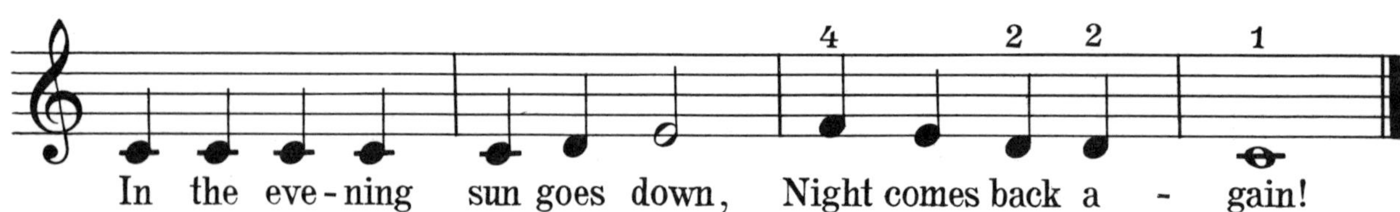
4 2 2 1
In the eve-ning sun goes down, Night comes back a - gain!

MARY HAD A LITTLE LAMB

Folk Song

3 2 1 2 3
Ma-ry had a lit-tle lamb, Lit-tle lamb, lit-tle lamb,
3 2 1 2 3 2 1
Ma-ry had a lit-tle lamb, its' fleece was white as snow.

$\frac{4}{4}$ - There are 4 equal quarter notes in a measure.
𝅗𝅥 - Half note, gets 2 counts.
♩ - Quarter note, gets one count.
𝅝 - Whole note - gets 4 counts.
A quarter note gets one beat or count.

GO TELL AUNT RHODIE

OUT TO
LUNCH

Teach: Skips (third, fifth)

Folk Song

Go tell Aunt Rho - die, Go tell Aunt Rho - die,
Go tell Aunt Rho - die, Her old gray goose is gone!

Teach: Bass Clef, 𝄢; L. H. fingering

Folk Song

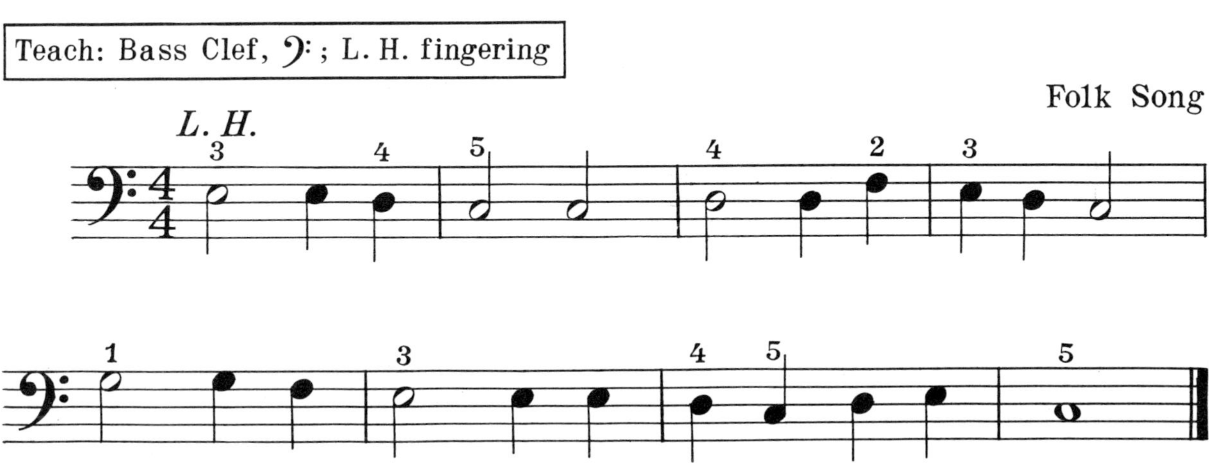
L. H.

𝄢 - Shows the F below middle C. The two dots are on either side of the F line.

THE CUCKOO

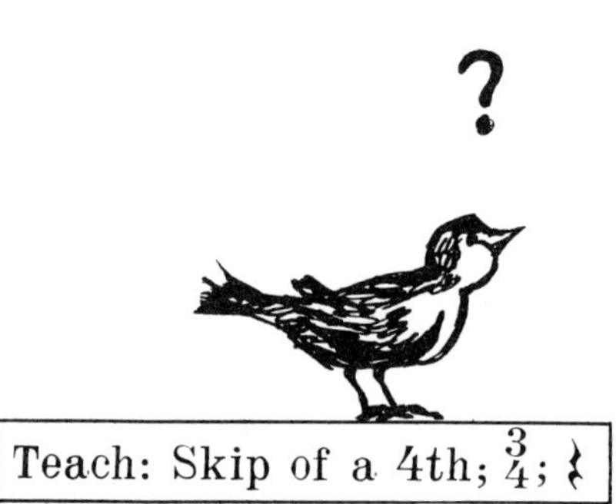
?

Teach: Skip of a 4th; $\frac{3}{4}$; 𝄽

German Folk Song

5 3 4 3 2
Cuck - oo, cuck - oo, song of the spring,
5 4 3 2 1
Cuck - oo, cuck - oo, hear the birds sing.
2 4 2 3 5 3
Sing in the morn - ing, sing in the eve - ning,
5 3
Cuck - oo, cuck - oo, hear the birds sing.

$\frac{3}{4}$ - There are three equal quarter notes to a measure. A quarter note gets one beat or count.

𝄽 - Quarter rest - a rest equal to a quarter note.

HOT CROSS BUNS

Teach: Hands alone, then combining; dynamics; eighth notes (♫)
Allegretto
English Folk Song
f Hot cross buns, mf hot cross buns.
One a pen - ny, two a pen - ny, f Hot cross buns.
p

2/4 - There are two equal quarter notes to a measure. A quarter note gets one beat or count.

♫ - Eighth notes

f - *forte* (loud)

mf - *mezzo forte* (medium loud)

p - *piano* (soft)

< - *crescendo, cresc.* (gradually getting louder)

LAVENDER BLUE

Teach: Shifting melody from hand to hand; 𝅗𝅥. = ♩ ♩ ♩

English Folk Song

Moderato
4 3 1
Lav - en - der
blue, dil - ly, dil - ly,
Rose - mar - y
green;
mp
5 1 2

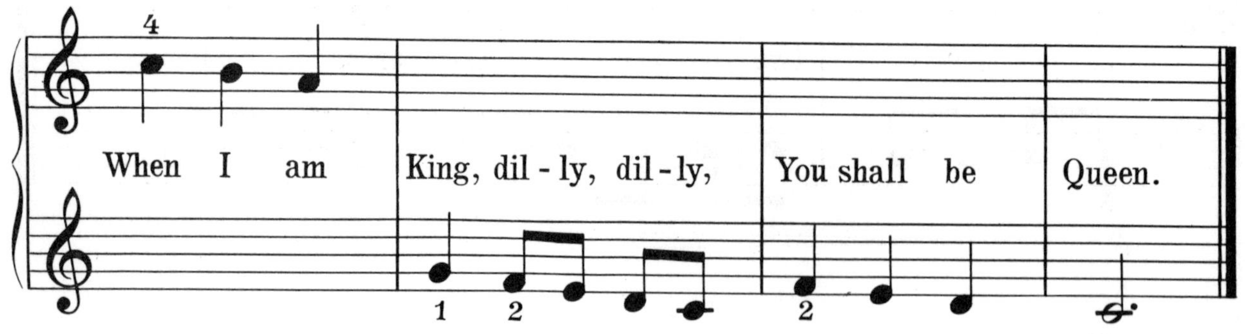
4
When I am
King, dil - ly, dil - ly,
You shall be
Queen.
1 2 2

Moderato - A medium speed; not fast, not slow.

mp - *mezzo piano* (medium soft)

𝅗𝅥. - The dot after the note increases the value by one half

DRINK TO ME ONLY WITH THINE EYES

Teach: Tie
BEN JONSON
Old English
Andante
mf
Drink to me on - ly with thine eyes And I will
pledge with mine.
mp
Or leave a kiss with -
in the cup, And I'll not ask for wine.

The curved line is a "tie". Hold the second note for its full value, but as the tie connects it to the first note, you don't strike it again.

Andante - Walking speed, not fast.

OATS, PEAS, BEANS

Teach: ▬ used as a whole measure rest; ♩. = ♪♪♪ ; ♪

Traditional English

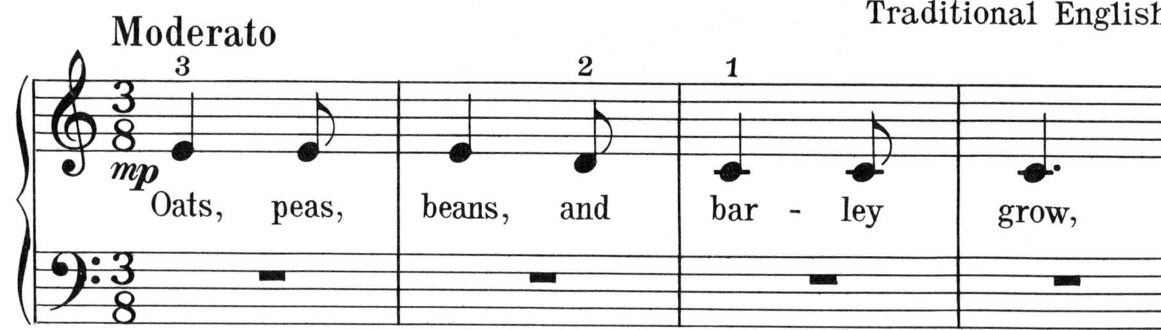
Moderato
mp
Oats, peas, beans, and bar - ley grow,

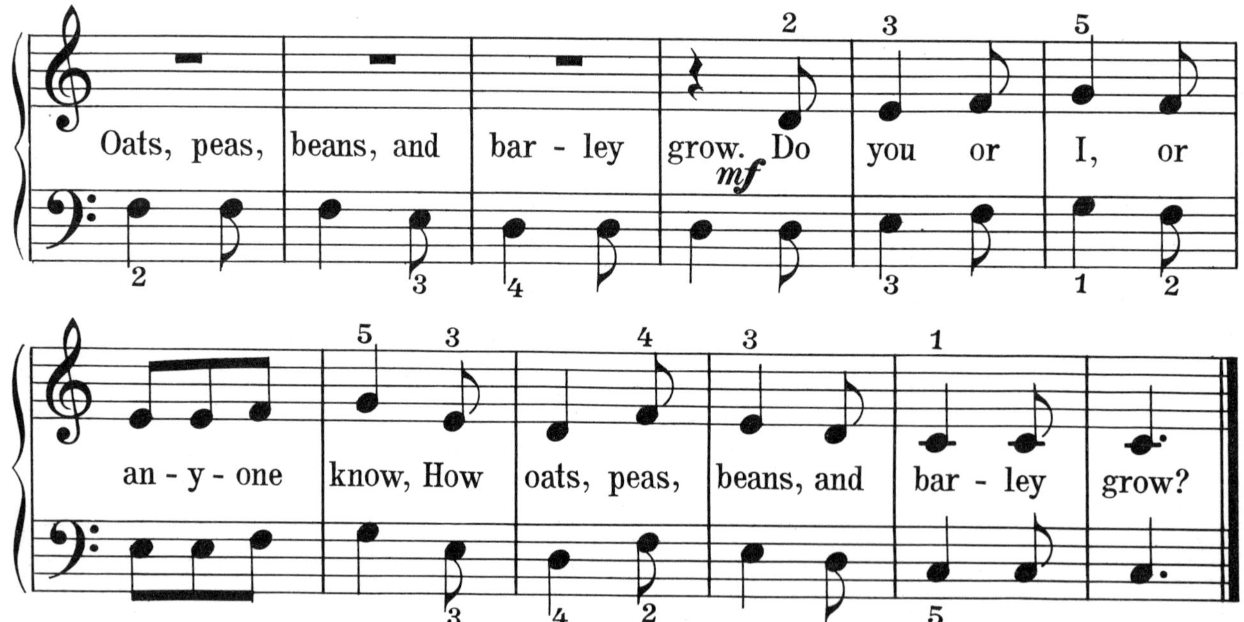
Oats, peas, beans, and bar - ley grow. Do you or I, or
mf
an - y - one know, How oats, peas, beans, and bar - ley grow?

$\frac{3}{8}$ - Three even eighth notes to a measure. An eighth note gets one beat or count.

♪ - Eighth note

♩. - The dot after the note increases the value by one half ♩. = ♪ ♪ ♪

▬ - Whole rest, shows a whole measure rest.
The whole rest hangs from the 4th line of the staff.
It is a rest equal to a whole note.

THE FARMER IN THE DELL

Teach: Slur; 6/8; last measure has only five eighths because of the eighth note up-beat; key of F (B♭)
Traditional English
mf
The farm - er in the dell, The
farm - er in the dell, Heigh - o, the
der - ry - o, The farm - er in the dell.

$\frac{6}{8}$ - Six even eighth notes to the measure. If played fast, $\frac{6}{8}$ has two beats to the measure, ♩♪♪ ♩♪♪, and is counted in 2.

𝄾 - Eighth rest - a rest equal to an eighth note.

♪♪♪ - The curved line over a series of notes shows that they are all one phrase (a musical thought, or idea) and usually means to play the notes *legato* (connected).

♭ - flat. A flat in front of a note tells you to play the note a half step lower.

THE BLUE TAIL FLY

Teach: L. H. changing clefs; A, G leger lines; 𝄐; key of G, F sharp.

Allegretto

Folk Song

Jimmy crack corn, and I don't care, Jimmy crack corn, and I don't care, Jimmy crack corn, and I don't care; Old mas - sa's gone a - way.

𝄐 - Fermata. A hold. The fermata increases the value of the note or rest over which it is placed (usually half again as long as the same note without this sign).

♯ - sharp. A sharp in front of a note tells you to play the note a half step higher.

Allegretto - Lively, but slower than *Allegro* (fast).

MERRILY WE ROLL ALONG

Teach: ♪. ♬ as ♬♬ . Contrast between even eighth note pattern and dotted eighth and sixteenth; sixteenth notes

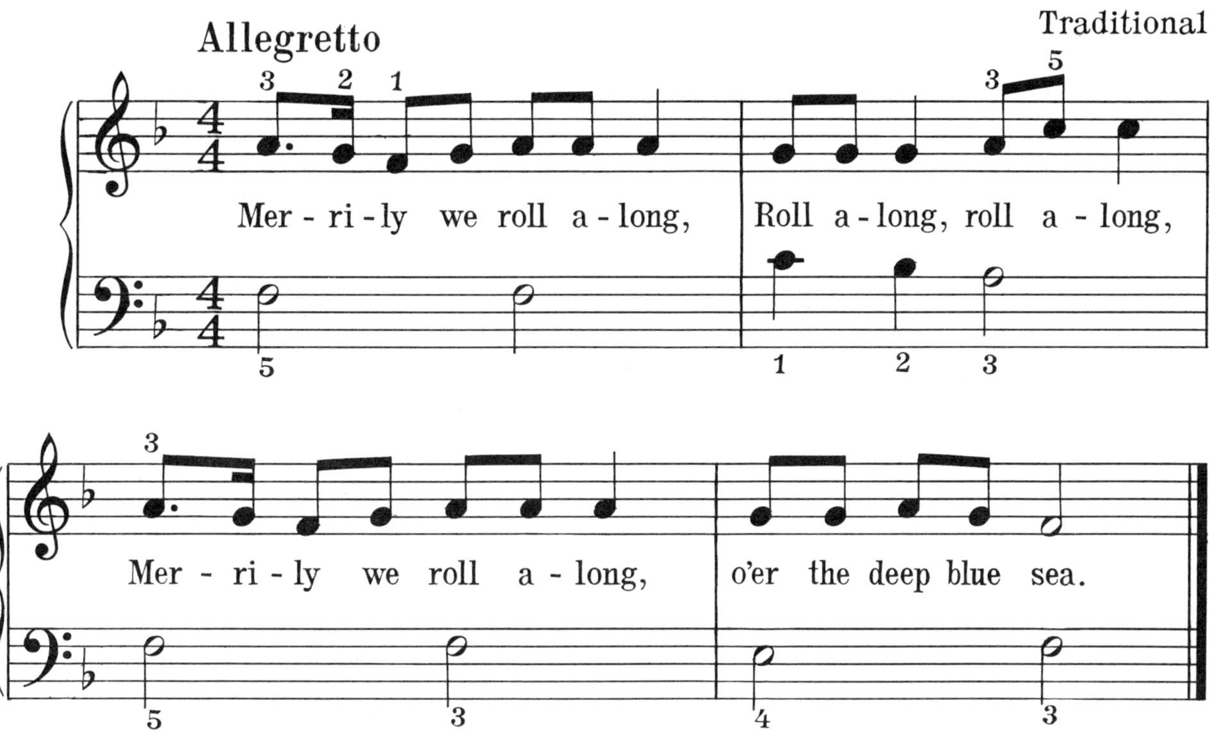
Allegretto
Traditional
Mer - ri - ly we roll a - long,
Roll a - long, roll a - long,
Mer - ri - ly we roll a - long,
o'er the deep blue sea.

♬ - sixteenth notes. There are four sixteenth notes in a quarter note.

PEASE PORRIDGE

Teach: Independence of hands.
Learn hands separately

Traditional

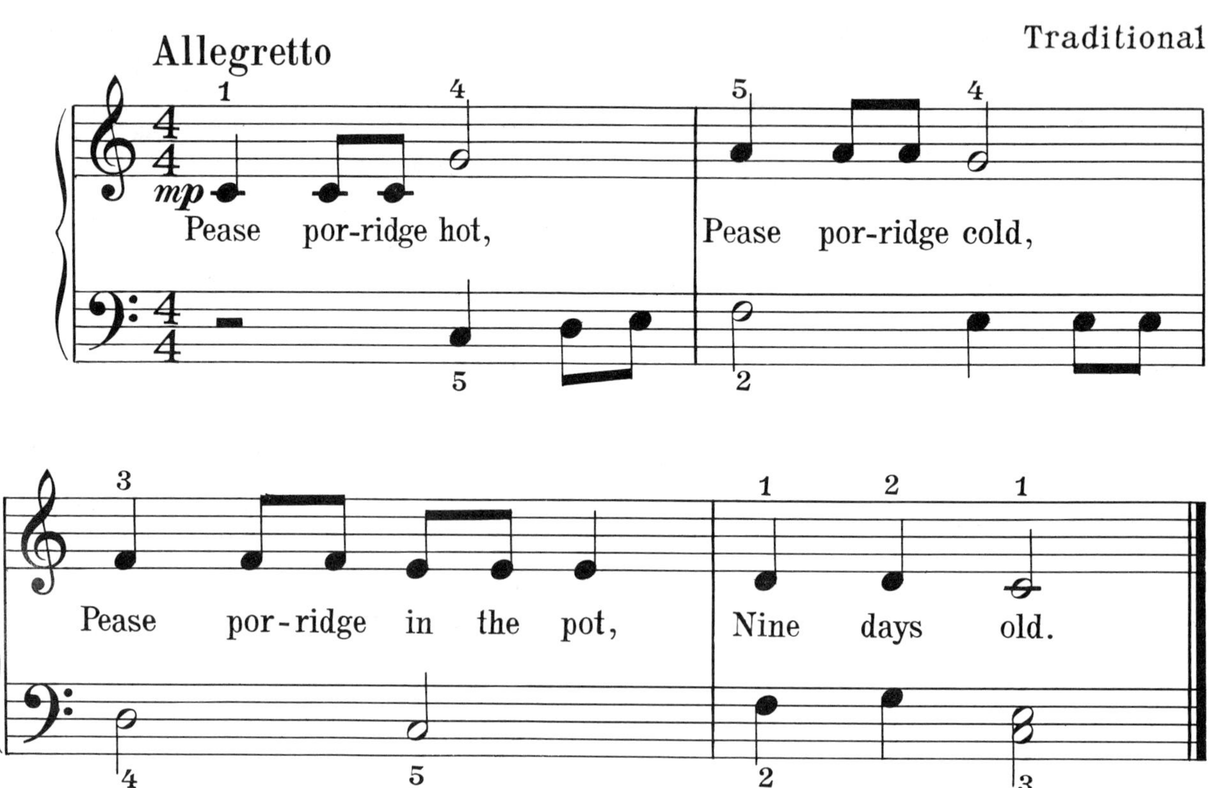
Allegretto
mp
Pease por-ridge hot,
Pease por-ridge cold,
Pease por-ridge in the pot,
Nine days old.

▬ - Half rest - a rest equal to a half note.

HOME
SWEET HOME

TEN LITTLE INDIANS

Teach: Dissonant passing tone in 1st and 4th measure; >; accidental

Traditional

Allegro
1 3 5 3 1 2 5 3 3 1
One little, two little, Three little Indians, Four little, five little, Six little Indians,
1 2 3 3 2

3 1 5 4 3 2 1
Seven little, eight little, Nine little Indians, Ten little Indian boys!
1 3 5

Allegro - fast

> - accent, heavy

♯ - sharp. The accidental is not found in the key signature. It alters the note through the whole measure, but is canceled by the bar line at the end of the measure.

LONDON BRIDGE

> Teach; L. H. entrance on 4th beat.
> Count out loud 1 - and - 2 - and, etc.

English Folk Song

Allegretto

mf

London bridge is falling down,
Falling down, falling down,
London bridge is falling down,
My fair Lady.

BLOW THE MAN DOWN

Teach: Independent voices in each hand; smooth connected fingerings; :‖

Sea Chantey

Andantino

mf

1. As I was a - walk-ing down Pa - ra - dise street, Way! Hey! Blow the man down! 1. A pret - ty young mai - den I chanced for to meet. Give me some time to Blow the man down.

2. Says she__ to me__ "Will you stand a treat?" Way! Hey! Blow the man down! 2. "De - light - ed says I," For a charm - er so sweet. Give me some time to Blow the man down.

Andantino - moving, a little faster than *Andante*.

:‖ - Repeat sign. Go back to the beginning, and play again.

THE OLD GRAY MARE

Teach: syncopation; cautionary accidentals;
¢; shifting R. H. fingering.
Allegretto
The old gray mare she
ain't what she used to be,
Ain't what she

¢ - $\frac{2}{2}$, two even half notes to the measure. A half note gets one beat or count.

(♮) - Cautionary accidental. The brackets ( ) around the natural show that this accidental is just a reminder. The change in the measure before is canceled by the bar line.

used to be, ain't what she used to be, The
old gray mare she ain't what she
used to be, Man - y long years a - go.

ACH, DU LIEBER AUGUSTIN

Teach: Contrasting *staccato* and *legato*
Tempo di Valse
mf
Ach, du lie - ber Au - gu - stin, Au - gu - stin,
Au - gu - stin, Ach, du lie - ber Au - gu - stin,

Tempo di Valse - The Waltz is a dance in $\frac{3}{4}$ time. This piece is one of the oldest waltzes. It was composed by a medieval wandering folk singer and comedian named Augustin.

♩̣ - staccato. The dot over the note head means to play the notes detached.

al - les ist hin.
Weib ist hin,
Hof ist hin,
Weib ist hin,
Hof ist hin.
Ach, du lie-ber Au - gu - stin,
al - les is hin.

SUR LE PONT d'AVIGNON

Teach: Changing fingers on a repeated note; practice L. H. as block chords

French Folk Song
Allegretto
mf legato
Sur le pont d'Av - i - gnon L'on y dan - se,
L'on y dan - se,
mp
Sur le pont d'Av - i - gnon,
L'on y dan - se tout en rond.

RING AROUND A ROSY

Traditional
Moderato
mp
Ring a - round a ro - sy,
Pock - et full of po - sy,
Ash - es, ash - es, We all fall down.

ROW, ROW, ROW YOUR BOAT

Teach: Key of D; *legato-staccato* contrast

Allegro
Row, row, row your boat, Gen - tly down the
stream, Mer-ri - ly, mer-ri - ly, mer-ri - ly, mer-ri - ly,
Life is but a dream.

SKIP TO MY LOU

Teach: Independence of hands (learn separately); L.H. imitating R.H.
Allegro
Folk Song
Flies in the butter- milk, shoo, shoo, shoo,
Flies in the butter-milk, shoo, shoo, shoo,
Flies in the butter-milk, shoo, shoo, shoo,
Skip to my Lou, my dar - ling.

A-HUNTING WE WILL GO

Teach: Melody shifting hands; L.H. accidentals and leger lines; turning second finger over thumb

Allegro
Traditional
Oh, a - hunt-ing we will go, A - hunt-ing we will go, We'll catch a lit-tle fox. And put him in a box, A - hunt-ing we will go.
Fat Box

BROTHER JOHN
(FRÈRE JACQUES)

Teach: round
Moderato
French Folk Song
mf
Are you sleep - ing, are you sleep - ing?
Broth-er John, Broth-er John? Morn-ing bells are ring-ing,
mf
Are you sleep-ing, are you sleep-ing? Broth - er John,
morn-ing bells are ring - ing, Ding, dang, dong, Ding, dang, dong!
Broth - er John? Ding, dang, dong!

Round-Both parts have the same melody, but they begin at different times. This is the simplest form of counterpoint (melody against melody)

AMERICA

Teach; Shifting L.H. positions; octave jump in L.H.

SAMUEL F. SMITH

HENRY CAREY

Maestoso
mp My coun-try! 'tis of thee, Sweet land of lib - er - ty,
Of thee I sing;
mf Land where my fa - thers died! Land of the
Pil-grims' pride!
f From ev - 'ry mount-tain side Let free-dom ring.

Maestoso - Majestic, slow.

ROCKABYE, BABY
Teach: Hold notes to the rests, not through them: play two octaves higher for music box effect.
Play both hands 2 octaves higher than written.
Gently rocking
R.H.
L.H.
mp
Rock-a-bye, baby, on the tree top, When the wind blows, the
cra-dle will rock; When the bough breaks, the cra-dle will
fall, And down will come ba-by, cra-dle and all.
rit.

rit. -*ritard, ritardando.* Gradually slower.

MARY HAD A LITTLE LAMB

Teach: Crossing hands; L.H. repeated pattern; use of pedal

Traditional
Andante
mp
p
r.h.
l.h.
Ma - ry had a
lit - tle lamb, Lit - tle lamb, lit - tle lamb, Ma - ry had a
lit - tle lamb, Its fleece was white as snow.
r.h.
Ped.

THERE'LL BE A HOT TIME IN THE OLD TOWN TONIGHT

Lively march tempo
THEO A. METZ
f When you hear The bells go ding, ling, ling,
All join 'round, And sweet-ly you must sing, And when the
verse is through, In the cho-rus all join in, There'll be a
hot time in the old town to - night.

DARK EYES

Teach: Syncopation, the L.H. holding across the bar; key of D minor; 𝄾̄

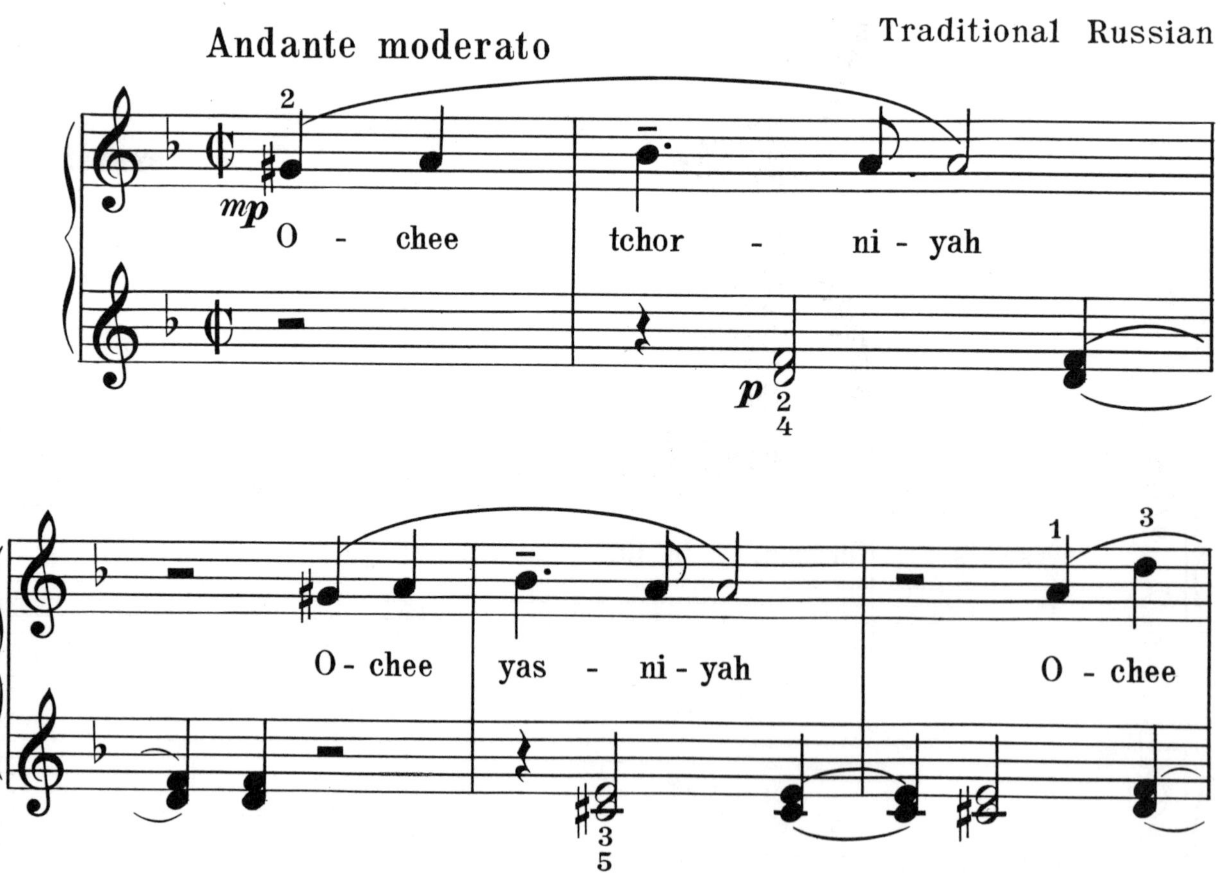
Andante moderato
Traditional Russian
mp
O - chee tchor - ni - yah
p
O - chee yas - ni - yah
O - chee

𝅘𝅥 - Hold the note for its full value. Tenuto mark.

szgoo - chee-ya
Ee - pre - kras - ni - ya
Leesh oo - vee - diel vass
Paw - tie - ryal paw - koy
Ee vies meer za - bill
Dlya nie - ya od - noy.

OH, SUSANNA

Allegretto

STEPHEN FOSTER

mf

I__ come from Al - a - ba - ma With my ban-jo on my knee, I'm__ going to Lou - 'si - an - a, My__ true love for to see. It__ rained all day the

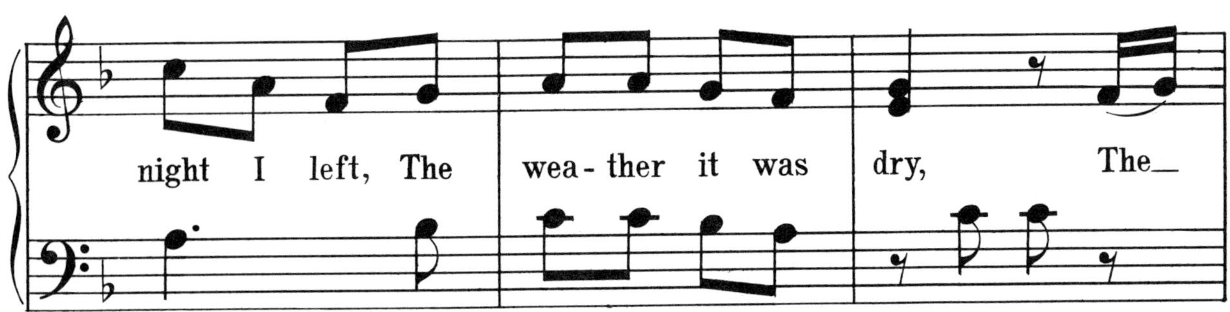
night I left, The
wea - ther it was
dry, The_

sun so hot I
froze to death, Su -
san - na don't you
cry.
2
1

3
5
2
4
2
Oh, Su -
san - na, oh
don't you cry for
me, For I
1
2

3
1
5
3
4
2
come from Al - a -
ba - ma With my
ban - jo on my
knee.
5
3
5

THE BAND PLAYED ON

Teach: Leger line notes

JOHN F. PALMER

CHARLES B. WARD

Waltz tempo

mf

Ca - sey would waltz with the straw - ber - ry blonde, And the band played on! He'd glide 'cross the floor with the girl he a - dored, And the band played

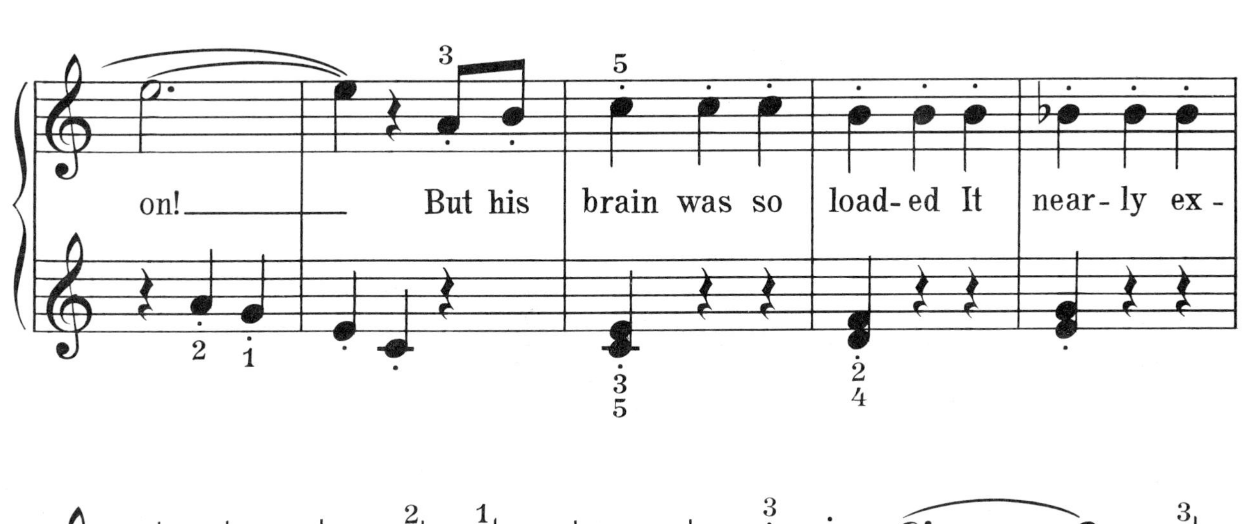
on!
But his
brain was so
load-ed It
near-ly ex-

plod-ed. The
poor girl would
shake with a-
larm.
He'd

ne'er leave the
girl with the
straw-ber-ry
curl, And the

band
played
on!

SHOO FLY

Teach: Tone cluster; ^

Traditional

Allegretto
Shoo fly, don't both - er me, Shoo fly, don't
(fly swatter)
both - er me, Shoo fly, don't both - er me, For
I be - long to some - bod - y!

^ - A heavy accent

HERE WE GO 'ROUND THE MULBERRY BUSH

Traditional

Allegretto
Here we go 'round the mul-ber-ry bush, the mul-ber-ry bush, the mul-ber-ry bush.
Here we go 'round the mul-ber-ry bush, so ear - ly in the morn - ing.

HYMN OF THANKSGIVING

Dutch Hymn

Moderato

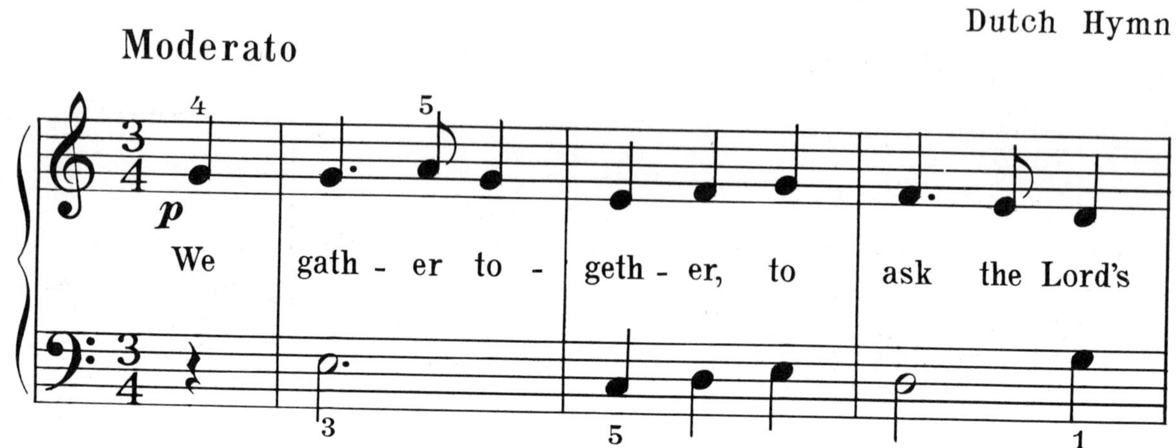
4
5
p
We gath - er to - geth - er, to ask the Lord's
3
5
1

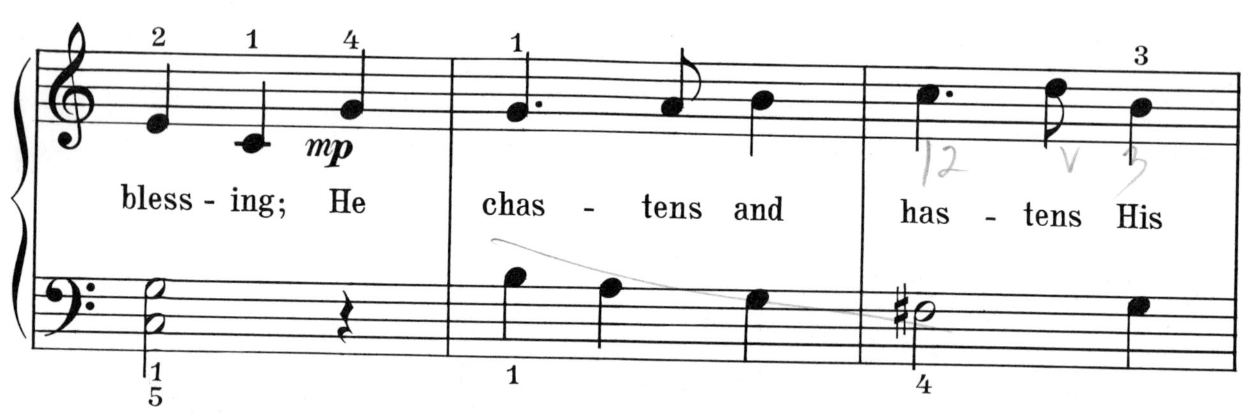
2 1 4
1
3
mp
bless - ing; He chas - tens and has - tens His
1
5
1
4

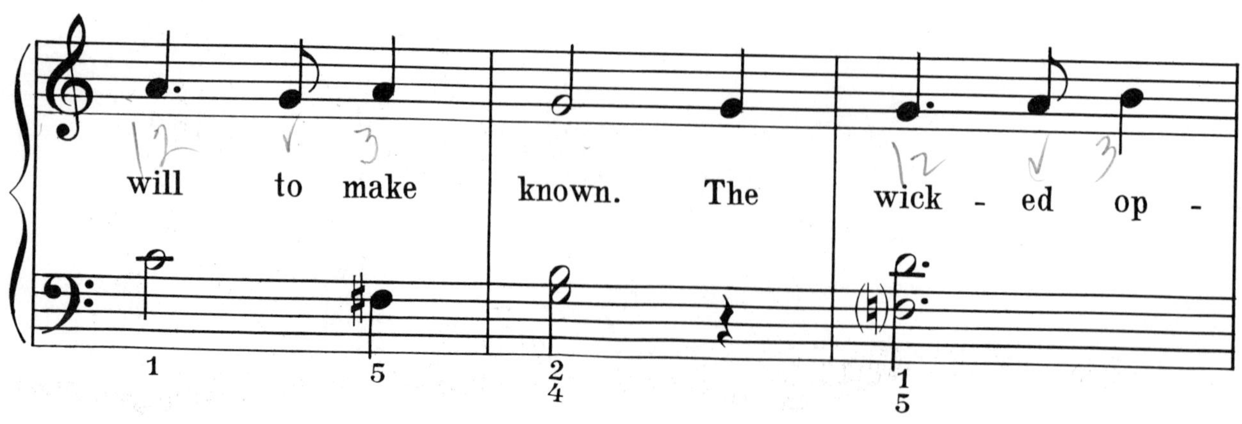
will to make known. The wick - ed op -
1
5
2
4
1
5

press - ing, now cease from dis -
tress - ing. Sing prais - es to His
name; He for - gets not His own.

THE BEAR WENT OVER THE MOUNTAIN

Teach: A-B-A form; connected L.H. chords

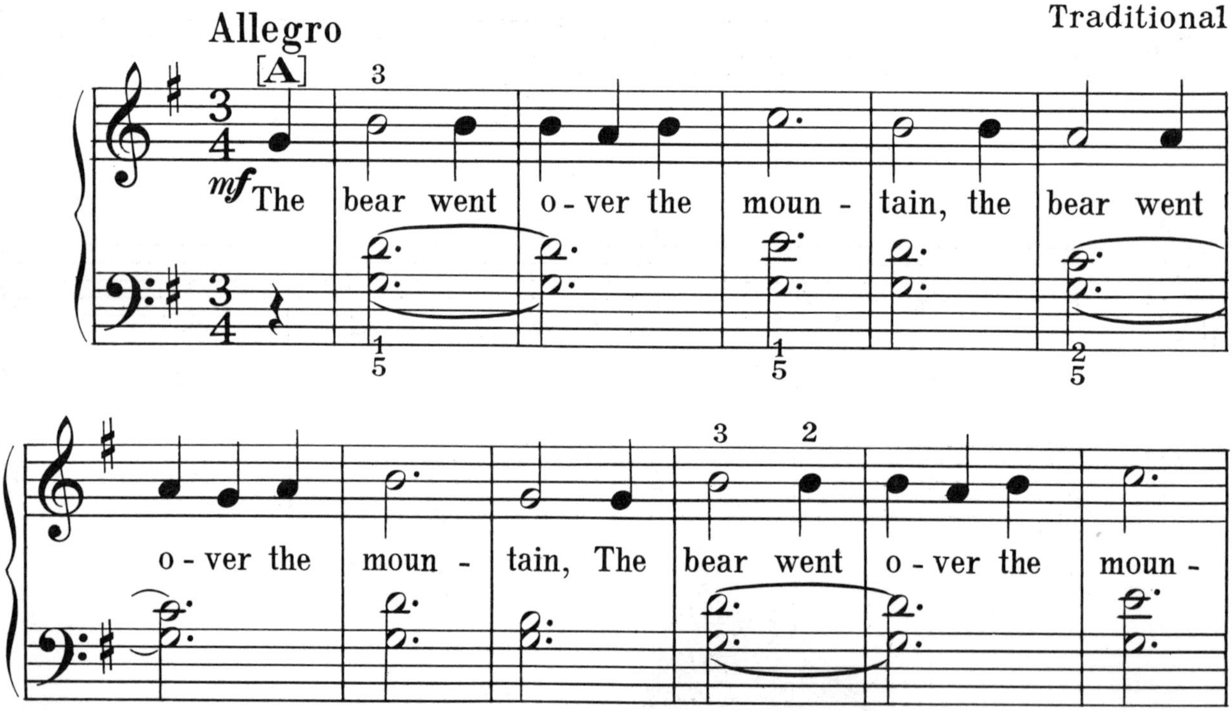

Allegro

Traditional

[A]

mf The bear went o - ver the moun - tain, the bear went o - ver the moun - tain, The bear went o - ver the moun - tain, to see what he could see.

[B]

To

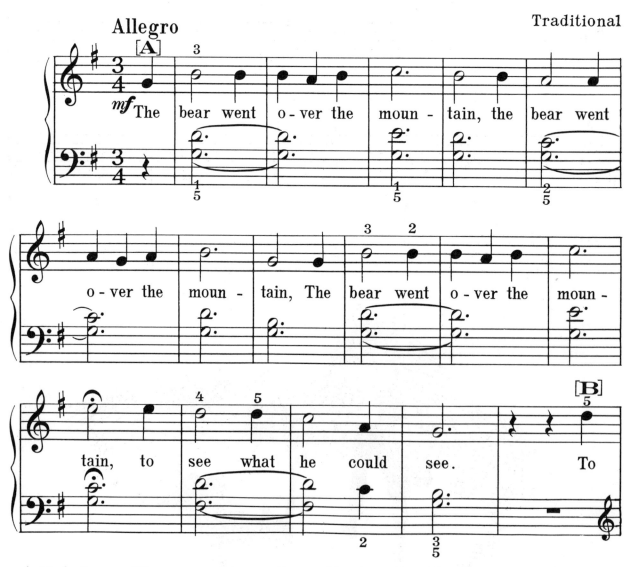

A-B-A form - Three part song form. Notice that the first and third sections are alike. This is also called "ternary" form.

see what he could see, to see what he could
see, The bear went o - ver the moun - tain, the
[A]
bear went o - ver the moun - tain, The bear went
o - ver the moun - tain, to see what he could see!

TWINKLE, TWINKLE LITTLE STAR

Teach: 8va; contrasting dynamics; *staccato* R.H. against *legato* L.H.

Words by JANE TAYLOR

Traditional

Allegretto
8va
sempre pp
Twin - kle, twin - kle lit - tle star,
crescendo
mp

8va
How I won - der what you are.
decrescendo

crescendo - gradually growing louder (*cresc.*, ——)

decrescendo - gradually growing softer (*decresc.*, ——)

sempre - always

8va
Up a - bove the world so high,
8va
Like a dia - mond in the sky,
8va
Twin - kle, twin - kle lit - tle star.
crescendo
8va
How I won - der what you are.
decrescendo

AU CLAIR DE LA LUNE

Teach: Style. This is arranged in an impressionistic style typical of recent French composers; moving thirds in both hands.

J. B. LULLY

Andante
pp
legato
Au clair de la lu - ne, Mon a - mi Pier - rot,

Prê - te - moi ta plu - me Pour é-crire un mot;

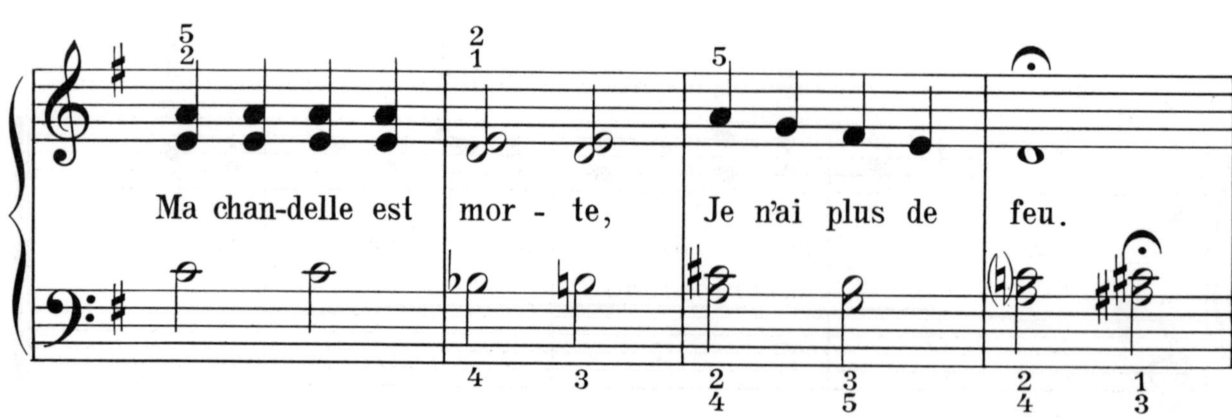
Ma chan-delle est mor - te, Je n'ai plus de feu.

3
1
Ou-vre-moi ta
por - te,
Pour l'a-mour de
Dieu.
3

This is the melody of "Au Clair De La Lune." Notice how the harmonization above changes the whole sound.

Andante

DU, DU, LIEGST MIR IM HERZEN

Teach: Waltz style
German Folk Song
Waltz time
mp
Du, du, liegst mir im Her - zen,
Du, du, liegst mir im Sinn;
mf
Du, du, machst mir viel Schmer - zen,

Waltz style-The Viennese waltz calls for a slightly stretched up-beat (the third beat of the measure), shown here with a tenuto sign (♩̲).

Weisst nicht wie gut ich dir bin!
Ja, ja, ja, ja,
Weisst nicht wie gut ich dir bin.

OLD MAC DONALD HAD A FARM

Teach: The sound of contemporary harmonies. This is arranged with clashing sounds that add to the interest for performer and listener. Play the R. H. alone first to get the melody firmly in mind.

Traditional

Moderato
modern chords
f Old Mac Don-ald had a farm, *mf* Ee - i, ee - i -
o! *f* And on this farm he had a duck,
mf Ee - i, ee - i - o! With a "Quack,quack" here and a

3
"Quack, quack," there, Here a "Quack," there a "Quack,"
4
Ev - 'ry - where a "Quack, quack." Old Mac Don - ald
rit.
had a farm, Ee - i, ee - i - o!

HOME ON THE RANGE

Teach: Rhythmic independence of the hands.

Moderato

Cowboy Song

mf Oh, give me a home, where the buf - fa - lo roam, Where the

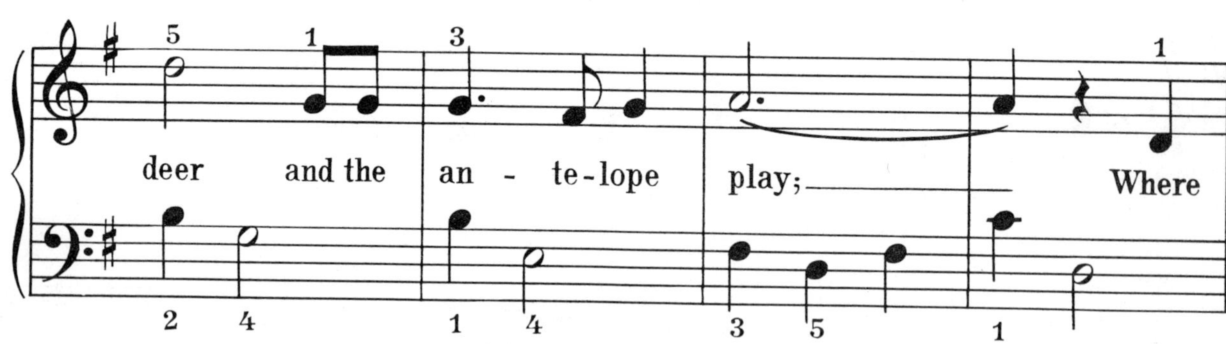
deer and the an - te - lope play; Where

sel - dom is heard a dis - cour - ag - ing word, And the

skies are not cloud - y all day.

5
Home, home on the range, Where the
1 5 1
3
deer and the an - te - lope play; Where
1 1
3 4
sel - dom is heard a dis - cour - ag-ing word, And the
1 5 2
2
skies are not cloud - y all day.
1 1 2 4

MARINES' HYMN

Teach: March time. ♩ = 120 is standard marching speed; syncopation; work out L. H. as block chords.

I. Z. PHILLIPS

March time

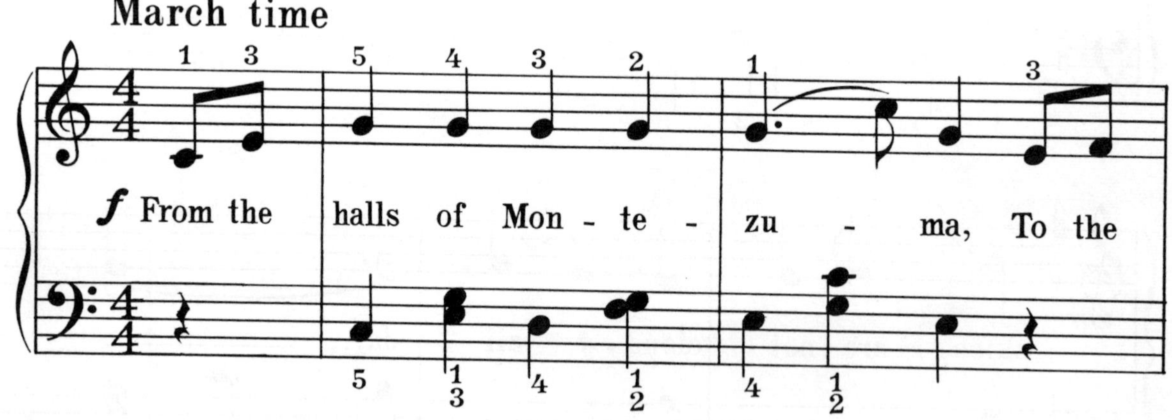
f From the halls of Mon - te - zu - ma, To the

shores of Tri - po - li, We___ fight our coun - try's

bat - tles, In the air, on land, and sea. First to
3 1 3

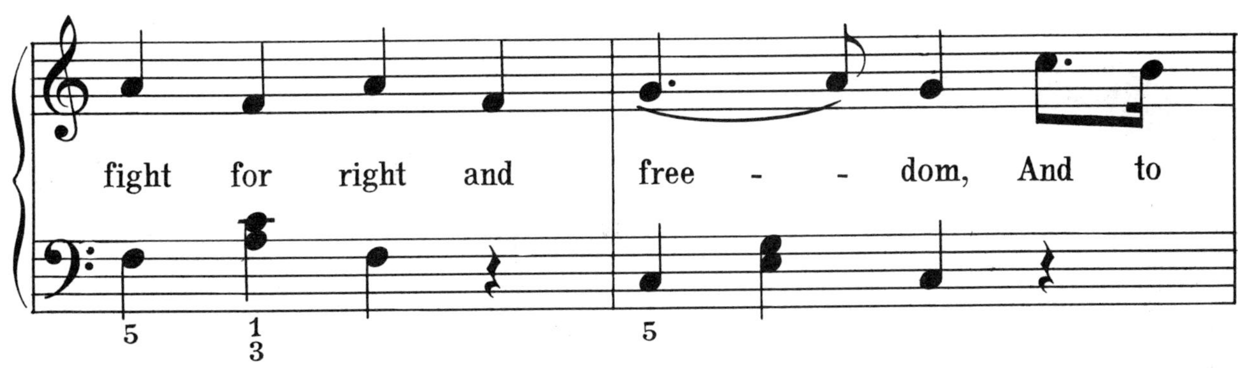
fight for right and free - - dom, And to
5 1 3 5

keep our hon-or clean; We are proud to claim the
5 5 4

ti - - tle of U - ni - ted States Ma - rines.
4 1 3 1 5 4 1 2

WHEN JOHNNY COMES MARCHING HOME

Teach: Minor keys; accented chords using body weight.
Traditional
Slow march tempo
mf When John-ny comes march - ing home a - gain, Hur -
rah, Hur - rah! We'll give him a heart - y

wel - come then, Hur - rah, Hur - rah! The
men will cheer, the boys will shout, The la - dies they will
all turn out, And we'll all feel gay When
John - ny comes march - ing home.

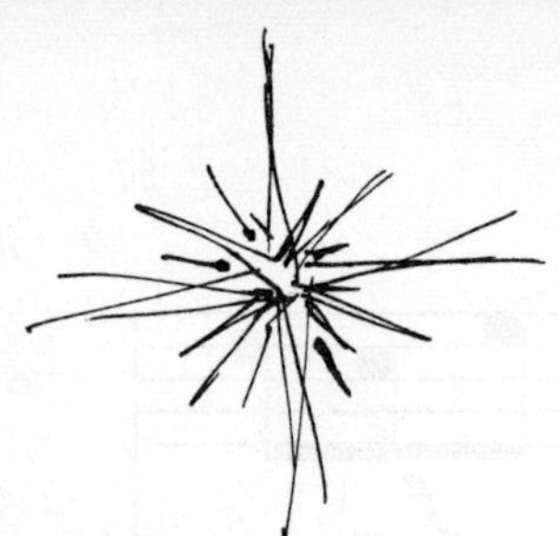

AWAY IN A MANGER

Teach: Moving thirds in R.H. with connecting fingerings; 𝄞 in L.H.; suspensions.

Words by MARTIN LUTHER

Christmas Carol

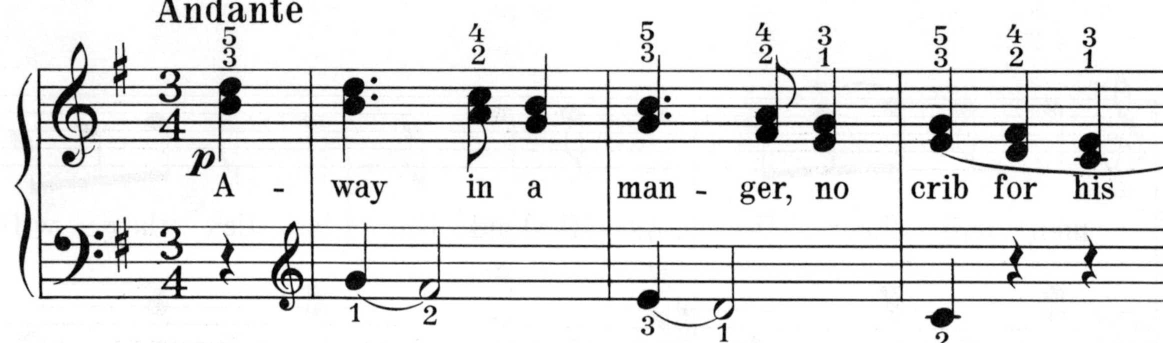

Andante
p
A - way in a man - ger, no crib for his

bed, The lit - tle Lord Je - sus laid down His sweet

head, The stars in the sky looked down where He

lay, The lit - tle Lord Je - sus a - sleep on the hay.

SHENANDOAH

Teach: Rhythm - count 1 - & - 2 - & - 3 - &, etc. to keep even;
1st and 2nd endings; repeat signs; legato fingering.
Sea Chantey
Andante moderato
Oh Shen-an - doah, I long to hear you. A - way, my roll-ing riv - er! Oh, Shen-an - doah, I can't get near you. A-way, a - way, I'm bound a - way, 'Cross the wide Mis-sou - ri! Oh Shen-an -
doah, I love your daugh-ter. A - way, my roll-ing riv - er! She lives a - cross the storm-y wa - ter. A-way, a - way, I'm bound a - way, 'Cross the wide Mis-sou - ri!

𝄆 𝄇 - Repeat the music between these bars.

1. 2. - the first time, play the first ending; the second time, skip the first ending and play the second ending.

Andante moderato - a moderate walking speed. A little faster than *Andante*.

STAR SPANGLED BANNER

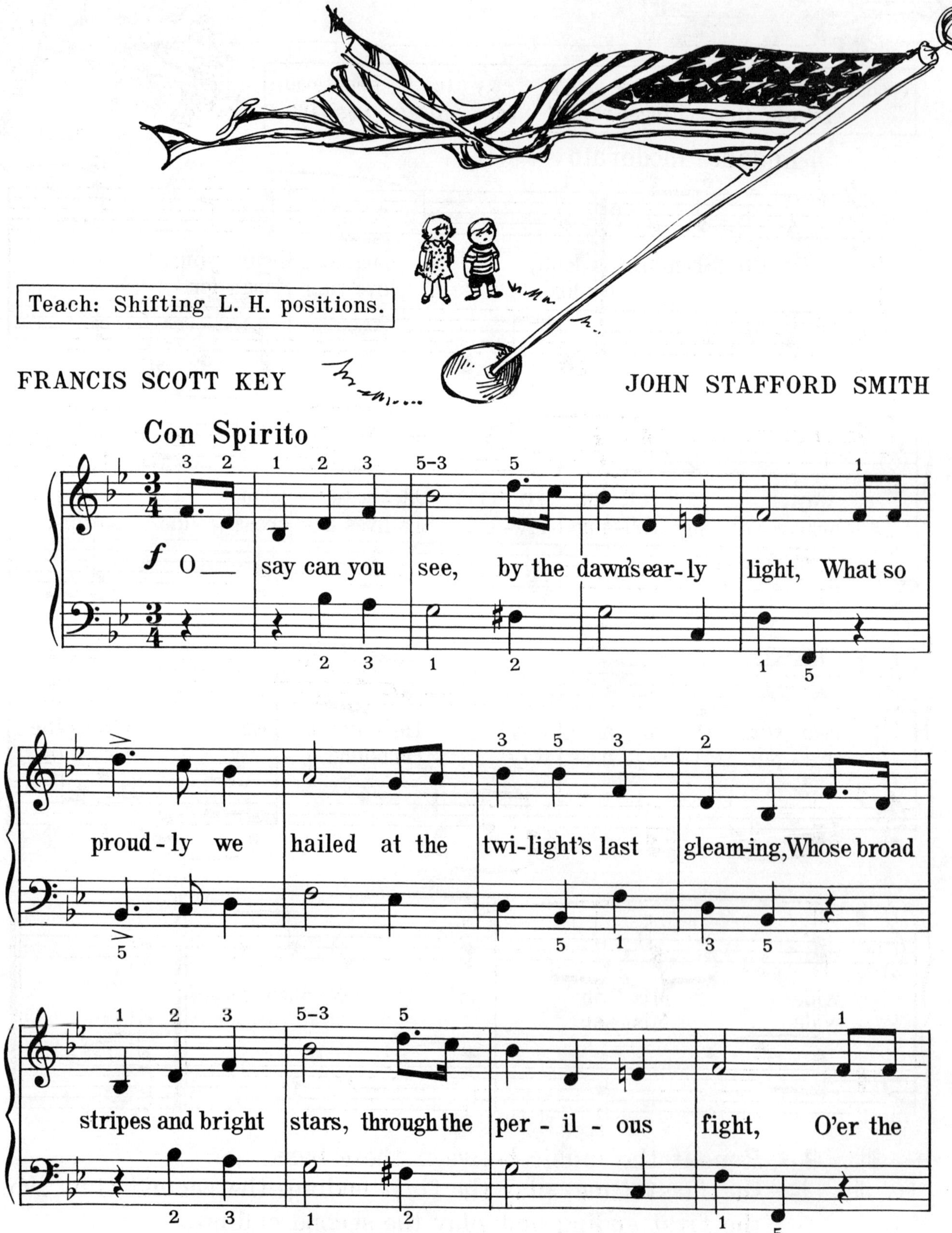
Teach: Shifting L. H. positions.
FRANCIS SCOTT KEY
JOHN STAFFORD SMITH
Con Spirito
O— say can you see, by the dawn's ear-ly light, What so
proud-ly we hailed at the twi-light's last gleam-ing, Whose broad
stripes and bright stars, through the per - il - ous fight, O'er the

ram - parts we watched were so gal - lant - ly stream-ing? And the
mf
rock- et's red glare, the bombs burst-ing in air, Gave
proof through the night that our flag was still there. O
f
say, does that star-span-gled ban - ner yet wave O'er the
land of the free and the home of the brave?

JINGLE BELLS

Teach: L.H. light *staccato,* R.H. smooth *legato*

J PIERPONT

Allegretto
Dash-ing through the snow, In a one-horse o-pen sleigh,

O'er the fields we go, Laugh-ing all the way;

Bells on bob-tail ring, Mak-ing spir-its bright;

Oh what fun it is to sing A sleigh-ing song to - night!
Jin-gle bells, jin-gle bells, jin-gle all the way!
Oh, what fun it is to ride in a one horse o - pen sleigh!
Jin - gle bells, jin - gle bells jin - gle all the way!
Oh, what fun it is to ride in a one-horse o - pen sleigh!

BAA, BAA, BLACK SHEEP

Teach: Melody singing out over moving lower parts; independent hands with smooth finger action and quiet hands.

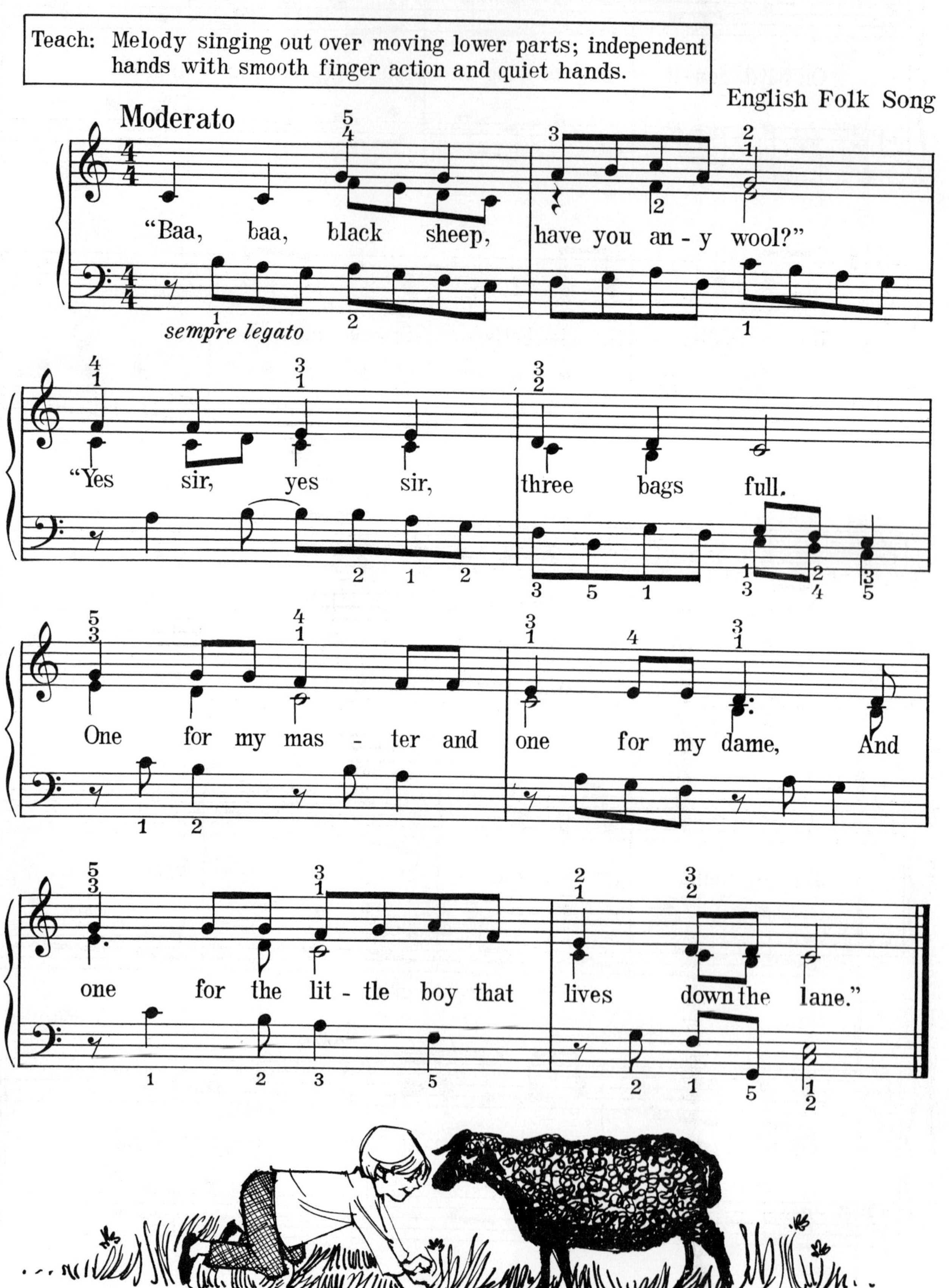
English Folk Song
Moderato
"Baa, baa, black sheep, have you an - y wool?"
sempre legato
"Yes sir, yes sir, three bags full.
One for my mas - ter and one for my dame, And
one for the lit - tle boy that lives down the lane."

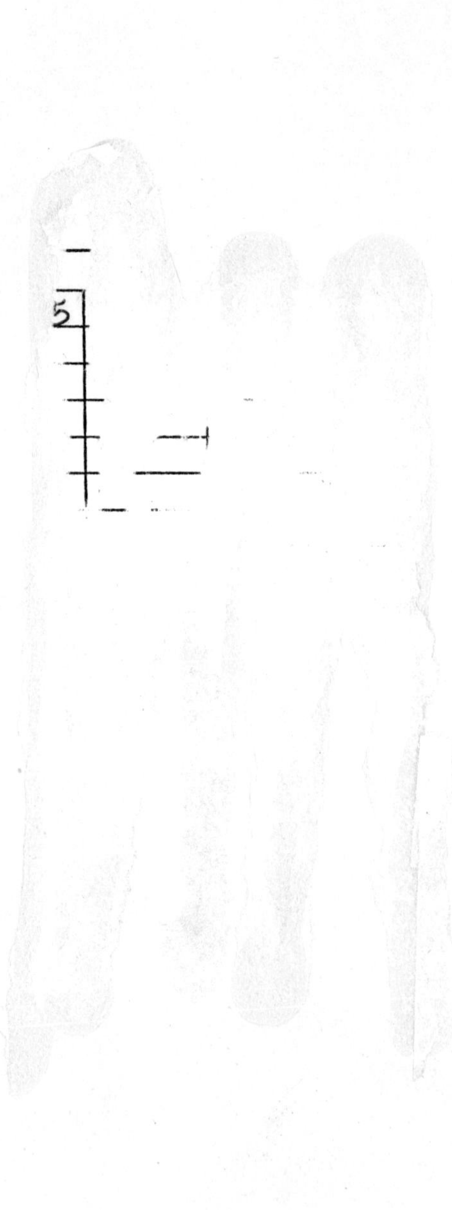